Organic
ACO...
DAIR...

ATKINSONS
COFFEE ROASTERS

Almond
Breeze

CAKESMITHS
THE COFFEE SHOP CAKE SPECIALISTS

HASBEAN

Olam
Specialty
Coffee

Victoria Arduino

1905

FOR BREW FREAKS, BEAN GEEKS

AND THE SIMPLY CURIOUS...

© Salt Media Ltd 2019
Published by Salt Media Ltd 2019

www.saltmedia.co.uk
Tel: 01271 859299
Email: ideas@saltmedia.co.uk

Salt Media *Independent Coffee Guide* team:
Richard Bailey, Katie Comer, Nick Cooper, Sophie Ellis,
Clare Hunt, Kathryn Lewis, Abi Manning, Tamsin Powell, Jo Rees,
Rosanna Rothery, Amy Sargeant, Christopher Sheppard,
Dale Stiling, Mark Tibbles, Selena Young and Josephine Walbank.
Design and illustration: Salt Media

A big thank you to the *Independent Coffee Guide* committee
(meet them on page 280) for their expertise and enthusiasm,
our headline sponsors iZettle and KeepCup **and sponsors** Acorn
Dairy, Atkinsons, Blue Diamond Almonds, Cakesmiths, Hasbean,
Henny & Joe's, Indy Coffee Box, Olam Specialty Coffee and
Victoria Arduino.

Coffee shops, cafes and roasteries are invited to be included in
the guide based on meeting criteria set by the committee, which
includes the use of speciality beans, providing a high quality
coffee experience for visitors and being independently run.

For information on *Independent Coffee Guides* for Ireland,
Scotland and The South & South Wales, visit:

www.indycoffee.guide
🐦 📷 @indycoffeeguide

LOCALLY
SOURCED

LYLE'S GOLDE

№ 164
Ginger & Co.

№73
Jaunty Goat Coffee

CONTENTS

page

WELCOME TO
BAYLEYS

DRINKING IN

WEL
COME

Bayley's of Bromsgrove Nº171

It's fair to say that, ever since the first edition of the *Northern Guide* was published five years ago, the coffee community has been super keen for us to include the Midlands in the book. So I'm thrilled to (finally) be able to introduce the first ever *North, Midlands & North Wales Independent Coffee Guide.*

Keen to discover exactly what caffeinated thrills the middle of England has to offer, in early summer a small contingent of the Indy Coffee crew hit the road on a week-long road trip. With the help of our pro committee and readers, we rounded up a series of must-visits and, after one too many flat whites (and way too many cinnamon knots) returned with the epic line-up of venues collated here.

It's not just fresh finds across England's heartland that we've discovered recently. The hefty size of this fifth edition also hints at the thriving state of the North and North Wales speciality scenes. It's been great to witness so many businesses expanding to open second, third and fourth outposts, while a number of roasteries have introduced cafes of their own. A whopping 241 caffeinated finds await in the biggest *Indy Coffee Guide* yet.

Enjoy.

Kathryn Lewis
Editor
Indy Coffee Guides

🐦 📷 @indycoffeeguide

WE HEARD YOU

Say hello to the new KeepCup Brew 6oz

This is the cup that started
the reuse revolution.

Made to be loved and looked after.

Use it and join the movement.

Reuse it and change the world.

Don't waste today.

keepcup.com

BE A HOME BREW *HERO*

So you've got a stock of speciality beans and brewing gear, but do you know how to use them to create game-changingly good coffee?

Matthew Wade – founder, head roaster and licenced Q grader at Hundred House Coffee – reveals the brewing basics

A E R O P R E S S

Saturate and let it sit for 30 seconds

YOU'LL NEED

AeroPress
Quality coffee beans
Burr grinder
Digital scales
Timer

MEASUREMENTS

Water **200g**
Coffee **15–18g**

'Wetting the filter serves a dual function,' says Matt. 'It helps the filter adhere to the cap and heats your brewing vessel'

METHOD

BOIL AND GRIND Bring the water to the boil and weigh out the coffee depending on your preferred strength. Grind it to a texture slightly finer than sea salt.

FILTER Insert a paper filter into the AeroPress' detachable plastic cap. Use some of the hot water to wet the filter and cap.

ASSEMBLE Assemble the AeroPress. Make sure the entire assembly is dry, as any residual moisture can compromise the device's seal.

TARE THE WEIGHT Place the AeroPress on the scales with the flared end up (the numbers should appear upside-down), then tare the weight.

ADD THE COFFEE AND WATER Add the ground coffee, being careful not to spill any into the ring-shaped gutter at the top of the AeroPress. Start a timer. Add twice the weight of water than you have grounds (e.g. for 15g coffee, add 30g water). The water should be about 94°c.

SATURATE AND SIT Make sure the coffee is saturated evenly, tamping slightly if necessary, and let it sit for 30 seconds.

FILL THE CHAMBER Use the remainder of the hot water to fill the chamber. After 1 minute, stir the grounds 10 times to agitate.

APPLY THE PRESSURE Fasten the cap, ensuring it locks into the grooves tightly. Flip the whole assembly over with haste and control. Position it on top of your brew vessel and begin applying downward pressure. If the pushing feels too easy, the grind is too coarse; if it's very hard to push, the grind is too fine. The coffee is fully brewed once it begins to make a hissing sound.

FRENCH PRESS

YOU'LL NEED

French press
Quality coffee beans
Burr grinder
Tablespoon
Digital scales
Timer

RATIO

Coffee **1g** : water **16g**

MEASUREMENTS

Water **1l**
Coffee **60-70g**

METHOD

GRIND Weigh out then grind the coffee and place into the plunger. The grind should be medium-coarse.

WEIGH THE WATER Boil the water and weigh it out – it should be around 95°c.

TICK TOCK Start the timer and pour the water over the grounds. After 4 minutes, stir with a tablespoon and gently push the floating crust of coffee downwards and leave to settle for at least another 4 minutes.

SCOOP Remove any floating coffee particles from the surface and discard.

PLUNGE Push the plunger very gently until just under the surface of the brew (not all the way to the bottom of the jug).

POUR Using the plunger as a filter for any remaining floating particles, gently pour into a cup.

'Be careful not to grind too coarse,' says Matt

Plunge ... until just
under the surface

DRIP FILTER

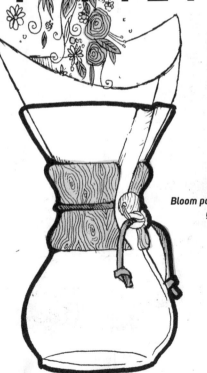

Bloom pour ... watch the grounds expand

YOU'LL NEED

Coffee dripper
(such as V60, Kalita
Wave or Chemex)

Filter paper

Quality coffee beans

Burr grinder

Pouring kettle

Digital scales

Timer

RATIO

Coffee **1g** : water **16g**

MEASUREMENTS

Water **384-432g**

Coffee **24-27g**

*'The spiralling
creates
a gentle
turbulence
that stirs
the coffee,
allowing the
water to more
evenly extract
the grounds,'
says Matt*

METHOD

POUR Place the filter paper in the drip brewer.
Pour boiling water through the filter paper to
rinse thoroughly.

GRIND Weigh out the coffee and grind it to a
medium consistency.

TAP TAP TAP Place the coffee in the filter paper within
the brewer and tap the sides so it settles evenly. Place
the brewer on your receptacle (such as a jug), then
place this on the scales and tare. If you're using a
Chemex, tare the entire thing.

WEIGH THE WATER Weigh out the hot water – it
should be just below boiling, around 95°c.

BLOOM POUR Start the timer and pour water slowly
from the centre outwards, saturating the grounds.
Pour about twice the amount of water to coffee initially
– this should take 30-40 seconds. The grounds will
expand and bloom.

TICK TOCK After 30-45 seconds, when the bloom
stops expanding, add the rest of the water in a steady
spiral towards the outer edge, pouring over dark or
bubbly patches if they appear.

WAIT All the water should have drained through the
coffee within 4 minutes.

DRINK Remove the brewer from the jug or remove
the filter paper from the Chemex and pour the
coffee into a cup.

YOU'LL NEED

Espresso machine
Quality coffee beans
Burr grinder
Digital scales
Timer

RATIO

Coffee **1g** : water **2g**

16g in : **32g** out

'Always begin with a clean, dry portafilter and flushed group head,' says Matt

METHOD

GRIND Weigh out then fine grind the coffee into the portafilter. You will need to adjust the grind size to reach your desired extraction time. If you change the grind size, discard a dose to prevent any of the previous grinds from entering the basket.

LEVEL AND BLESS Once the coffee is in the portafilter, give the side of the basket a couple of taps to level the coffee bed. If any coffee grinds are sitting on top of the rim, use a clean, dry finger to wipe them off – this is called blessing the portafilter.

VERTICAL TAMP Place the portafilter against the edge of a sturdy work surface so that the spouts overhang the edge of the counter. Insert the tamp onto the coffee bed, pressing down as flatly and evenly as possible. Stop pressing when you feel that the puck can no longer be compressed. Your wrist and elbow should be vertical above the tamp to prevent injury.

PREP Lock the portafilter in place in the machine and place a preheated cup under the spouts on top of the scales. Set the timer to zero and tare the scales.

BREW Press the brew button on the machine at the same time as you start the timer. Keep your eye on the weight; stop the timer and brewing 2-3g early – compensating for some drips – finishing close to your desired brew weight.

ADJUST With the desired weight reached, check the timer. If it's under the desired time, the coffee is under-extracted and will taste sour. If the timer extends longer, the coffee is over-extracted and will taste bitter.

Repeat the process with a finer grind if the timer was short or a coarser grind if the timer went over. Remember to make your tamping method as consistent as possible to remove unnecessary variables.

ESPRESSO

Level and bless the portafilter

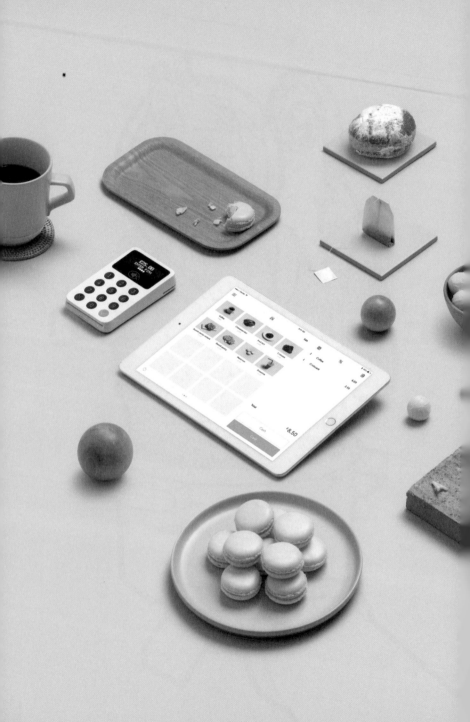

Tools to run your coffee shop

COFFEE MARKET

CRASH

The market price of coffee is at an all-time low. News headlines are suggesting that our morning flat white could become a thing of the past, while the implications for coffee-growing communities are dire. What's going on? **Kathryn Lewis** extracts some pertinent points and asks if speciality coffee could be the solution

Most latte lovers are used to seeing smiling images of coffee farmers on the walls of the big chain coffee shops. It suggests a straight line from crop to cup which supports those 'poor farmers' in underdeveloped parts of the world. Yet how many of us have any real understanding of how the coffee market works?

CRISIS ALERT

Earlier this year, it was brought to the attention of the masses when headlines announced the '2019 coffee crisis'. Anxiety-stricken coffee fans took to social media to retweet the impending coffee shortage and look for answers. However, all that became clear was that the coffee market is a lot more complex than those coffee shop posters would suggest.

So should we be stockpiling beans for a coffee apocalypse? Apparently not. *'It's actually the production of too much coffee that has caused the market price to crash to an all-time low,'* explains speciality green bean importer Phil Schluter of Liverpool's Olam Specialty.

'They're flooding the market and driving down the price'

'Next year, Brazilian farmers will produce their biggest ever crop. They're flooding the market and therefore driving down the price. The devaluation of the Brazilian currency and their move to mechanical farming techniques (more machines, less paid workers) means they are one of the few countries that still sells profitably to the New York market at current levels, albeit only just,' says Phil.

The volume of coffee in the market is putting a huge amount of pressure on other coffee-growing regions and farmers are being paid less for their beans as a result of the over-supply. Margins are already eye-wateringly tight for growers and now some are moving away from coffee in order to farm more lucrative crops such as macadamia nuts and avocados. That's the best-case scenario: others are simply going hungry.

'We're seeing serious malnourishment and a drop in the number of children going to school in coffee-growing regions due to the fall of the market,' says Phil.

SOLUTIONS IN SPECIALITY?

Most of the large coffee chains serve commodity coffee, yet there's a thriving speciality sector built on ethical principles which has long championed paying a fair price to farmers. So where does this fit in?

'We pay around two to three times the futures coffee [commodity grade] market price when buying speciality coffee,' explains Phil. *'So one of the ways struggling farmers can survive is to aim for a higher cup profile and, therefore, a higher price for their greens.*

'Roasters, cafes and consumers need to understand that buying speciality grade coffee is the difference between children eating or going hungry – we can quickly forget that low coffee prices have a real life-changing effect on farmers around the world.'

'Buying speciality grade coffee is the difference between children eating or going hungry'

Frequenting cafes that source beans from indie specialist roasteries (which are transparent about the prices they pay for beans) is one way coffee lovers can support struggling growers. It's a win-win as the higher grade product is also seriously delicious and offers far more complex flavours than dark-roasted commodity beans. You could liken it to the difference between a fine wine and a bottle of mid-priced plonk.

New roasteries crop up every month and others greenwash their products to imbue them with positive associations, so it's not easy or straightforward to discover exactly how ethical the coffee you're drinking might be.

'There are a lot of commodity roasteries using the speciality stance to gain mileage,' agrees Paul Meikle-Janney, co-founder of Dark Woods Coffee near Huddersfield.

'At Dark Woods we try to avoid any posturing and are always very careful in how we refer to the farmers we work with. When businesses refer to "our farmers", there's an uncomfortable neo-colonialism. We're not "saving" them, we're buying beans from them because they're skilled producers of quality ingredients that rightly deserve a higher price.'

LIVE AND DIRECT

In recent years, 'direct trade' has become a buzzword in the roasting community. Referring to the process where roasters buy beans direct from the farmers or mill owners rather than using an importer (such as Olam), it's often seen as a way of paying more to farmers and strengthening the relationship between them and the roastery.

'There are a lot of roasteries that use the term "direct trade" incorrectly,' says Paul. *'It's amazing how many you see shouting about how their coffees are directly traded who then go on to mention the importer they use as a middleman.*

'Farmers don't necessarily want to trade directly either,' continues Paul. *'Logistically, farmers want to sell coffee in volume which they can do via an importer who will then sell smaller amounts to a number of roasteries. If you're buying direct trade, you need to buy an awful lot to make it sustainable.*

'If a coffee isn't direct trade, it's certainly not a bad thing. When we use an importer, we still select the farms and work with people at origin to get the balance of varietals we're looking for. It doesn't have to be direct trade to be a direct relationship.'

What the fallout of the next big Brazilian harvest will be is impossible to tell. Yet consumers can help support the farmers by buying speciality grade coffee from ethical roasteries and choosing cafes that support them (as featured in this guide).

Asking about the beans and where they come from is important and any cafe or roastery worth their salt will be happy to explain their bean sourcing.

'If a coffee isn't direct trade, it's certainly not a bad thing'

The fact that most of the speciality indies are also small (and often family-run) businesses, which like the speciality coffee growers focus on crafting a top quality product, provides a pleasing parallel with what's going on at source. And when supporting them results in delicious coffee, it's not only our responsibility – it's also easy to do.

CONTINUE YOUR COFFEE ADVENTURES AT HOME

The new Indy Coffee Box subscription service delivers handpicked speciality grade beans from roasteries featured in the Indy Coffee Guides.

Each month, take a coffee road-trip across the UK and Ireland from the comfort of your kitchen.

Order the next box now at

INDYCOFFEEBOX.CO.UK

HOW TO USE THE GUIDE

№131
The Whaletown Coffee Company

CAFES

Find coffee shops and cafes where you can drink top-notch speciality coffee. We've split the region into areas to help you find places near you.

ROASTERIES

Discover leading speciality coffee roasteries and find out where to source beans to use at home. Find them after the cafes in each area.

MAPS

Every member cafe and roastery has a number so you can find them either on the area map at the start of each section, or on more detailed city maps.

MORE GOOD STUFF

Discover **more good coffee shops** and **more good roasteries** at the back of the book.

Don't forget to let us know how you get on as you explore the speciality cafes and roasteries.

🐦 📷 @indycoffeeguide

WWW.INDYCOFFEE.GUIDE

№ 118
Wired Coffee and Cake

NORTHUMBERLAND, TYNE AND WEAR
& COUNTY DURHAM

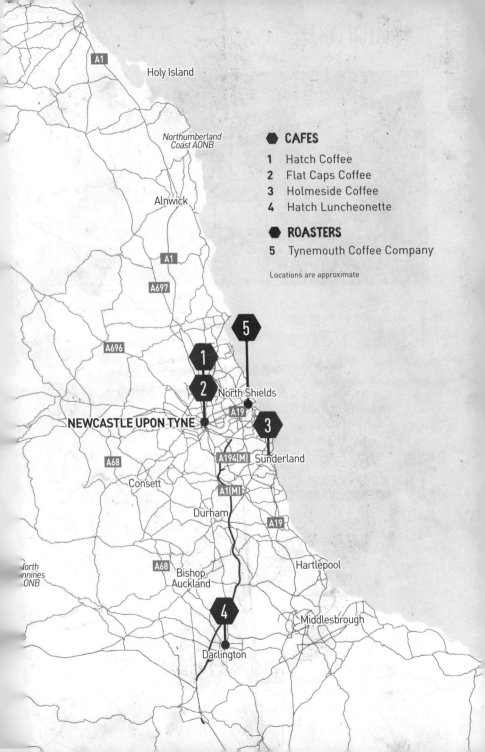

CAFES

1 Hatch Coffee
2 Flat Caps Coffee
3 Holmeside Coffee
4 Hatch Luncheonette

ROASTERS

5 Tynemouth Coffee Company

Locations are approximate

MAP№1 HATCH COFFEE

Former Parking Attendants' Cabin, Ellison Place, Newcastle upon Tyne, NE1 8XS

This tiny speciality shop perfectly demonstrates that a great cup of coffee comes down to a seemingly simple recipe: quality beans, decent kit and a skilled barista.

Hatch's humble set-up within a former parking attendants' cabin may lead you to wonder how such great things can be created in such a dinky interior, yet the team behind it have done an impressive job of reinvigorating the neglected space and filling it with the best products the local area has to offer. Awards a-plenty attest to the quality of Hatch's offering.

INSIDER'S TIP IN SUMMER, COOL DOWN WITH AN AFFOGATO OR A VEGAN PEANUT-CHIP ICE CREAM

Beans travel a ludicrously short distance from Pink Lane Coffee and reflect the harvest's seasonality. Head barista Mark Briston – who's explored the globe in his search for coffee knowledge – is as accomplished at pulling shots and fashioning latte art as he is at warmly welcoming customers to the to-go hotspot.

In addition to top-notch espresso, Mark serves devilishly tempting cakes and has recently added a milkshake range. The most popular flavour? Madagascan bourbon vanilla ice cream and single origin espresso.

ESTABLISHED
2016

KEY ROASTER
Pink Lane Coffee

BREWING METHOD
Espresso

MACHINE
La Marzocco Linea PB

GRINDER
Mythos One

OPENING HOURS
Mon-Fri
7.30am-4.30pm

www.hatchcoffee.com T: 07713 820905

f @hatchcoffeenewcastle   @hatchcoffee   @hatchcoffeenewcastle

ᴹᴬᵖ№2 FLAT CAPS COFFEE

9-11 Carliol Square, Newcastle upon Tyne, NE1 6UF

As Newcastle's speciality scene flourishes, the city's original gamechanger goes from strength to strength.

Founder Joe Meagher continues to focus on his trio of ambitions: exceptional coffee, excellent food and unfailingly friendly service. And with a central-as location and decor that splices industrial chic with lush hanging plants and festoon lights, Flat Caps is a hub for all manner of coffee fans.

INSIDER'S TIP HOSTING A PARTY? BOOK THE SPACE FOR YOUR NEXT EVENING KNEES-UP

While brews can be enjoyed courtesy of Kalita or AeroPress, it's the impressive oak and walnut syphon bar that takes centre stage: pull up a pew and watch the theatre of brewing in all its glory. While it's entertaining, it's the pursuit of incredible flavours that prevails, so only great beans get their go in the gear. Interesting lots are sourced from Flat Caps' roaster of choice, , with guests like Seth Taylor rounding out the offering.

A temptingly straightforward food menu includes breakfasty treats such as eggs bennie with haggis, and comforting dishes for carnivores, veggies and vegans.

ESTABLISHED
2010

KEY ROASTER
Hasbean

BREWING METHOD
Espresso,
AeroPress,
Kalita Wave,
syphon

MACHINE
Sanremo
Café Racer

GRINDER
Mahlkonig Peak,
Mahlkonig EK43

OPENING HOURS
Mon-Fri 8am-8pm
Sat-Sun 9am-6pm

Gluten FREE

BEANS AVAILABLE INSTORE

WIFI

DISABLED ACCESS

COFFEE COURSES

DOG FRIENDLY

---

www.flatcapscoffee.com   T: 01912 615748

f @flatcapscoffee   🐦 @flatcapscoffee   📷 @flatcapscoffee

MAP №3 HOLMESIDE COFFEE

Sunderland Museum & Winter Gardens, Burdon Road, Sunderland, Tyne and Wear, SR1 1PP

Coffee and food at British tourist spots are usually of an unremarkable – if not pretty poor – standard. So for Sunderland's speciality-savvy locals to make the cafe within the Museum & Winter Gardens their regular haunt for top-notch coffee is testament to the quality of the Holmeside experience.

Beans destined for the La Marzocco machine and batch and drip filter kit showcase some of the UK's roasting greats. The house coffee comes from the Cornish crew at Origin, while single origins from and Pink Lane alternate on the guest spot.

INSIDER'S TIP CHECK OUT THE NEW TAKEAWAY HATCH ACROSS TOWN AT THE OLD J&C POTTER NEWSAGENTS

It's not only the coffee that's impressive: Holmeside's epic brunch and lunch bill puts most other museum menus to shame. Dishes change regularly and include the likes of 12-hour beef brisket hash with wild mushroom jus, roasted broccoli, leeks and poached eggs. Plant-based visitors plump for pizza topped with cashew cheese, red onion and broccoli.

The unique venue also hosts monthly socials so it's worth lining up your visit to coincide with one of the food pop-ups, live music or DJ events.

ESTABLISHED
2013

KEY ROASTER
Origin Coffee Roasters

BREWING METHOD
Espresso, batch brew, filter

MACHINE
La Marzocco Strada EE

GRINDER
Mythos One

OPENING HOURS
Mon-Sat 9am-4.30pm
Sun 10am-4pm

T: 01915 618629
f @holmesidecoffee 🐦 @holmesidecoffee 📷 @holmesidecoffee

MAP № 4 HATCH LUNCHEONETTE

32 Blackwellgate, Darlington, County Durham, DL1 5HN

Hatch founders Jasmin and Phil Robson take great pride in providing Darlington dwellers with top-notch speciality coffee kicks.

The pocket-sized cafe was the first in the North East to install a Sanremo Café Racer and, with an exclusive house blend from Rounton and milk fresh from a herd of local cows, offers a one-of-a-kind caffeine experience.

The busy little kitchen knocks up a similarly drool-worthy bill of dishes: buddha bowls, sourdough sarnies and perfect poached eggs are all up for grabs. If it's sunny, take it alfresco in the new seating area.

INSIDER'S tip CHECK OUT THE SINGLE ORIGIN GUEST ON BATCH FILTER

The laws of nature state that great coffee and good food should always be followed by cake, and the Hatch crew have come up with a divine collection of confections including chocolate, hazelnut and ricotta, and hunks of blueberry, elderflower and lemon – all baked each morning by Jasmin and her mum Rosalie.

ESTABLISHED
2018

KEY ROASTER
Rounton Coffee Roasters

BREWING METHOD
Espresso, batch filter

MACHINE
Sanremo Café Racer

GRINDER
Fiorenzato F64 Evo

OPENING HOURS
Tue-Thu 8am-6pm
Fri 8am-8pm
Sat 9am-8pm
Sun 10am-4pm

T: 01325 380720

f @hatchluncheonette 🐦 @hatchlunch 📷 @hatchluncheonette

ROASTER

Photo: Nathan Dumlao

5 TYNEMOUTH COFFEE COMPANY

Prudhoe Street Back, North Shields, Tyne and Wear, NE29 6RE

The Tynemouth team have been putting their distinctive stamp on the North East's speciality scene for over a decade.

The guys have recently moved to new state-of-the-art facilities, enabling the building of a training centre as well as the installation of a beefier 20kg Toper.

Each carefully sourced bean that's hand-roasted on the new kit references the roastery's Geordie roots: blends include the 'Nee Caffeine Hinny' Mexican roast and 'Whey Aye Man', a globetrotting amalgam of beans from Costa Rica, Ethiopia and Colombia.

EACH CAREFULLY SOURCED BEAN THAT'S HAND-ROASTED... REFERENCES THE ROASTERY'S GEORDIE ROOTS.

The team are passionate about getting the local community brewing their coffee, so they offer barista courses for pros as well as home delivery in the Tynemouth area for caffeine fiends of the domestic variety.

ESTABLISHED
2009

ROASTER MAKE & SIZE
Toper 20kg
Toper 10kg
Toper 5kg

OPEN BY APPOINTMENT

COFFEE COURSES

BEANS AVAILABLE

www.tynemouthcoffee.com   01912 600995

@tynemouthcoffee   @tynemouthcoffee   @tynemouth_coffee

CUMBRIA, LANCASHIRE & MERSEYSIDE

Nº21
72 Degrees

CAFES

6 The Moon & Sixpence Coffeehouse
7 Homeground Coffee + Kitchen
8 Comida [food]
9 Atkinsons The Hall
10 Atkinsons The Music Room
11 Journey Social Espresso Bar
12 Exchange Coffee Company – Clitheroe
13 Brew + Bake
14 Cedarwood Coffee Company
15 Exchange Coffee Company – Blackburn
16 Siphon Espresso & Brew Bar
23 Caffè & Co.

ROASTERS

24 Carvetii Coffee Roasters
25 Red Bank Coffee Roasters
26 Mr Duffins Coffee
27 Rinaldo's Speciality Coffee & Fine Tea
28 Farrer's Tea & Coffee
29 Kircabi Roasters
30 Atkinsons Coffee Roasters & Tea Merchant
31 Exchange Coffee Company
32 Roberts & Co.
33 Django Coffee Co.

TRAINING

37 Caffè & Co.

Locations are approximate

Liverpool

● CAFES

17 Crosby Coffee
18 Root Coffee
19 Ropes and Twines
20 Bold Street Coffee
21 92 Degrees
22 Bean There Coffee Shop

⬡ ROASTERS

34 Crosby Coffee
35 Neighbourhood Coffee
36 92 Degrees and The Baltic Roastery

Locations are approximate

MAP 6 THE MOON & SIXPENCE COFFEEHOUSE

29 Main Street, Cockermouth, Cumbria, CA13 9LE

Cockermouth's original speciality coffee shop retains its rep as the town's go-to for great caffeine and quality home baking (including sourdough and incredible cakes).

Founder Stephen Kidd proudly champions the Cumbrian community and so the vast majority of produce featured on the food and drink menus is sourced within 17 miles of the cafe. This local-centric ethos even extends to the house espresso which is roasted down the road in Threlkeld by the gang at Carvetii.

INSIDER'S TIP TAKE IN A BAG OF BEANS FROM YOUR TRAVELS AND BARTER WITH THE BARISTAS

One exception to the rule is the monthly AeroPress guest coffees which are chosen by a different member of the Moon team each time. They enjoy picking up new and intriguing beans on their travels and often swap bags with customers, so the roll call of previously featured beans makes for a globetrotting line-up.

This isn't just a cake and coffee type of gaff as live music, food pop-ups, talks and workshops extend the opening hours for regular events.

ESTABLISHED
2016

KEY ROASTER
Carvetii Coffee Roasters

BREWING METHOD
Espresso, AeroPress, drip, cold brew

MACHINE
La Marzocco Linea PB

GRINDER
Mahlkonig K30 Air

OPENING HOURS
Mon-Sat 9am-5pm
Sun 10am-4pm

 Gluten FREE
 BEANS AVAILABLE INSTORE
 WIFI
 CYCLE FRIENDLY
 OUTDOOR SEATING
 BRING YOUR OWN Cup

www.the-moon-sixpence.business.site T: 01900 829378

f @sixandmoon @sixandmoon @sixandmoon

MAP № 7 HOMEGROUND COFFEE + KITCHEN

Main Road, Windermere, Cumbria, LA23 1DX

T ime seems to slow to a leisurely pace in the Lake District, and this easy-going vibe flows right through Windermere's charming neighbourhood cafe.

Day-trippers and locals pop into Homeground in search of great coffee, but often wind up staying for the long haul once they've spied the day's bakes and menu of seriously good grub. Don't be fooled by the tiny kitchen either: the crew deliver over 200 stonking brunches on a busy day.

INSIDER'S TIP ARRIVE EARLY ON THE WEEKEND – IT'S OFTEN PACKED WITHIN MINUTES OF OPENING

Whether you're swayed by the mega fried-chicken waffles or intrigued by the secret-recipe hash browns, pairing your pick of the seasonal menu with an espresso based brew from local roaster Carvetii is a no-brainer.

In the second hopper, guest roasts from the likes of Red Bank, Maude, Curve and Workshop feature. Opt for batch brew if you're fuelling the day's pursuits on-the-go or adjust to District time and savour a V60 pourover.

ESTABLISHED
2015

KEY ROASTER
Carvetii Coffee Roasters

BREWING METHOD
Espresso, V60, batch brew

MACHINE
La Marzocco Linea PB

GRINDER
Nuova Simonelli Mythos One x 2, Mahlkonig EK43

OPENING HOURS
Mon-Fri 8.30am-5pm
Sat-Sun 9am-5pm

Gluten FREE · BEANS AVAILABLE INSTORE · CYCLE FRIENDLY · OUTDOOR SEATING · DISABLED ACCESS

www.homegroundcafe.co.uk T: 01539 444863
f @homegroundcafe 🐦 @homegroundcafe 📷 @homegroundcafe

MAP №8 COMIDA [FOOD]

90 Highgate, Kendal, Cumbria, LA9 4HE

Forget mint cake and Cumberland sausage. These days Kendal is also known for its churros, tapas and mighty fine coffee – care of Comida.

Husband and wife team Simon and Alba have intertwined their Yorkshire and Valencian roots to create a menu that delights with its broad appeal: think slithers of salty jamón alongside rib-sticking cakes and you get the idea.

INSIDER'S tip INVEST IN A KEEPCUP AND SCORE A 20 PER CENT DISCOUNT ON TAKEAWAY DRINKS

The casual restaurant is bathed in light which streams through huge floor-to-ceiling windows and makes for an appealing spot in which to graze while soaking up industrial-refectory vibes.

Carefully roasted beans nip up the M6 from Atkinsons in Lancaster to Comida's trusty Sanremo Verona. And, while you'll want to pay homage to the expertly roasted coffee, it would be madness to stop at a flat white when there are spicy huevos rotos, grilled octopus and meatballs on offer.

ESTABLISHED
2017

KEY ROASTER
Atkinsons
Coffee Roasters

BREWING METHOD
Espresso, filter

MACHINE
Sanremo
Verona RS

GRINDER
Mythos One

OPENING HOURS
Tue 12pm-8pm
Wed-Sat 9am-8pm
Sun 10am-4pm

www.comidafood.co.uk   T: 01539 732082

f @comidakendal   🐦 @comida_kendal   📷 @comida_kendal

ATKINSONS THE HALL

10 China Street, Lancaster, Lancashire, LA1 1EX

Since Ian and Sue Steel took over Atkinsons Coffee Roasters in 2005, Lancaster has become a must-visit stop on any coffee crawl across northern England.

In addition to the roastery, they've opened three speciality cafes close by – the latest within the only contemporary wing of 11th century Lancaster Castle. And, while Atkinsons' impact on the northern scene permeates much further than the medieval town (find a fourth coffee shop in Manchester and Atkinsons beans in hoppers across the region), The Hall is at the heart of the operation.

INSIDER'S TIP SPECIALS INCLUDE JAPANESE ICED COFFEE AND ICED COCONUT MATCHA

At the core of the China Street HQ, between the cafe and beautiful original shop, is the new roastery which is kitted out with high-tech eco roasters and restored vintage models. Ask for a nose around the working art installation before taking a seat in the cafe to sample the latest single origin with a wedge of cake from the in-house bakery.

ESTABLISHED
2012

KEY ROASTER
Atkinsons
Coffee Roasters

BREWING METHOD
Espresso,
Chemex, syphon

MACHINE
Sanremo Café
Racer

GRINDER
Mythos One
Clima Pro,
Mahlkonig EK43

OPENING HOURS
Mon-Sat **8**am-**6**pm
Sun **10**am-**5**pm

www.thecoffeehopper.com   T: 01524 65470

f @thehallcafe   🐦 @coffeehopper   📷 @atkinsons.coffee

MAP № 10 ATKINSONS THE MUSIC ROOM

Sun Square, Sun Street, Lancaster, Lancashire, LA1 1EW

Speciality coffee shops are pretty good at breathing new life into old buildings, and this top-notch find inside a Rococo-era garden pavilion is one of the most notable transformations in the North.

Local roastery Atkinsons took over the ground floor of the Landmark Trust building in 2010, installing a contemporary bar for the preparation of interesting filters and crowd-pleasing espresso from beans roasted across the road at its China Street HQ.

INSIDER'S Tip CHECK OUT ATKINSONS' NEW VENUE AT LANCASTER CASTLE

In summer, the courtyard hums with customers drinking iced V60 and tucking in to homemade cakes, pastries and sandwiches. A new bill of craft beers and soft drinks means the lively hubbub often continues until close.

In winter, head indoors and grab one of the stools which line the window or squirrel yourself away on the cosy mezzanine level. Whatever the time of year, no trip is complete without a visit to Atkinsons' nearby retail store for freshly roasted beans, single origin chocolate and local artisan spirits.

ESTABLISHED
2010

KEY ROASTER
Atkinsons
Coffee Roasters

BREWING METHOD
Espresso, V60,
batch brew

MACHINE
Sanremo
Verona RS

GRINDER
Mythos One
Clima Pro,
Mahlkonig
Tanzania

OPENING HOURS
Mon-Sat 10am-5pm
Sun 11am-4pm

Gluten FREE

BEANS AVAILABLE INSTORE

WIFI

CYCLE FRIENDLY

OUTDOOR seating

DISABLED ACCESS

BRING YOUR OWN Cup

DOG FRIENDLY

www.thecoffeehopper.com   T: 01524 65470
f @themusicroomcafe   🐦 @coffeehopper   📷 @atkinsons.coffee

MAP № 11 JOURNEY SOCIAL ESPRESSO BAR

59 King Street, Lancaster, Lancashire, LA1 1RE

When it comes to perfect pours and artfully compiled brunches, the benchmark at this Lancaster hotspot is set pretty high.

Journey's founders poured huge amounts of energy into the creation of their contemporary new space, assembling the brew bar by hand and even stamping each table with the logo, so it's fitting that their team are equally committed to crafting excellent coffee and drool-worthy dishes.

INSIDER'S TIP THE TEAM HAVE WON A BEVY OF AWARDS INCLUDING LANCASHIRE'S BEST CAFE 2019

The kitchen crew are masters of the brunch universe: everything is made from scratch, from the fruit syrup drizzled over fat slices of sugar-dusted french toast to the vegan stack of sweetcorn and edamame fritters with mushrooms and house salsa.

Whichever vegan, veggie or carnivorous dish you finally decide upon, there's no need to deliberate over your coffee order as New Zealand's Allpress beans are simply prepared as filter or espresso (and served with milk from nearby Brades Farm).

ESTABLISHED
2018

KEY ROASTER
Allpress Espresso

BREWING METHOD
Espresso, AeroPress, V60, Delter Coffee Press

MACHINE
La Marzocco Linea

GRINDER
Victoria Arduino Mythos One

OPENING HOURS
Mon-Sat 8.30am-5pm
Sun 9.30am-4pm

 Gluten FREE
 BEANS AVAILABLE INSTORE
 WIFI
 OUTDOOR seating
 BRING YOUR OWN Cup
 COFFEE COURSES
 DOG FRIENDLY

T: 07561 550255

f @journey social espresso bar   🐦 @journeysocial1   📷 @journeysociallancaster

MAP 12 EXCHANGE COFFEE COMPANY – CLITHEROE
24 Wellgate, Clitheroe, Lancashire, BB7 2DP

If you're searching for a traditional coffee house experience, Exchange's Clitheroe venue (complete with William Morris wallpaper, antique furniture and a tea-caddy lined wall) presents the perfect opportunity to immerse yourself in timeless caffeine culture.

The handsome Victorian building on busy Wellgate unites cafe, roastery and shop under one roof. Its three floors offer ample seating space in which to stretch out and enjoy the house-roasted coffee and freshly prepped food.

INSIDER'S TIP EXCHANGE HAS TEAMED UP WITH A LOCAL CHOCOLATE CO TO CREATE A SPECIAL COFFEE BAR

Curious visitors can watch the action as small batches of ethically sourced beans are roasted daily on the Probat LN12 machine. And with a whopping 35 single origins and blends available at any one time, the team are constantly dealing with beans from different origins and tinkering with roast profiles.

Sample your pick of the batch as espresso, Clever Dripper or french press, then pair your poison with one of the hearty cakes or homemade lunches. If you're also into tea, there's a huge selection of loose-leaf infusions to explore.

ESTABLISHED
1991

KEY ROASTER
Exchange Coffee Company

BREWING METHOD
Espresso, Clever Dripper, french press

MACHINE
La Marzocco GB5

GRINDER
Mahlkonig K30, Ditting KR804

OPENING HOURS
Mon-Sat 9am-5.30pm

 Gluten FREE
 BEANS AVAILABLE INSTORE
 WIFI
 CYCLE FRIENDLY
 OUTDOOR seating
 DISABLED ACCESS
 BRING YOUR OWN Cup
 COFFEE COURSES

DOG FRIENDLY

www.exchangecoffee.co.uk   T: 01200 442270
f @exchangecoffeecompany @exchange_coffee @exchange_coffee

MAP № 13 BREW + BAKE

Preston Market, Earl Street, Preston, Lancashire, PR1 2JA

This little gem is to be found at the epicentre of Preston Market's new and contemporary glass, timber and steel home.

Refurbed and modernised in 2018, the hall proudly showcases the finest local produce, much of which Brew + Bake founder Julie Fausset uses when crafting artisan sandwiches, grilled cheese and cakes at her cafe.

After leaving a job in the NHS to pursue a career in hospitality, Julie's ambition soon became a family affair. Daughter Rebecca designed the stall based on markets she'd seen (and loved) in Europe, while husband Adrian and son Liam brought the vision to life by building the unit, which includes an awesome concrete counter.

INSIDER'S Tip CHECK THE CHALKBOARD FOR DAILY CHANGING FOOD SPECIALS

With the aim of sourcing locally and supporting other indies, Julie turned to Lakes roaster Carvetii for the Brew + Bake house beans. Each espresso and filter is served in a gorgeous Pilling Pottery cup which the team designed at the nearby studio.

ESTABLISHED
2018

KEY ROASTER
Carvetii Coffee Roasters

BREWING METHOD
Espresso, filter

MACHINE
Nuova Simonelli Appia II

GRINDER
Mahlkonig K30

OPENING HOURS
Mon-Sun 8am-4pm

---

www.brewandbakepreston.com T: 07971 999978

f @brewandbakepreston @ @brewandbakepreston

HERE TO HELP YOU GROW

Olam
Specialty
Coffee

Tel: +44 (0) 151 498 6500
Email: osceurope@olamnet.com
olamspecialtycoffee.com

MAP № 14 CEDARWOOD COFFEE COMPANY

10 Winckley Street, Preston, Lancashire, PR1 2AA

Steer off Preston's busy thoroughfare and into its ancient cobbled side streets to find this much-loved coffee shop refuge.

Weary shoppers, day-trippers and locals head here to refuel with top-quality coffee, fresh-off-the-griddle panini and flaky pastries.

On the coffee front, hero roasters Atkinsons, Red Bank and Dark Woods take turns on the Sanremo machine, while additional guest espressos provide yet more opportunities to change things up.

INSIDER'S TIP VEGAN OR DAIRY-FREE? THERE IS A GOOD SELECTION OF ALT MILKS AVAILABLE

Coffee classics are accompanied by affogato and espresso-spiked salted caramel milkshakes made with locally churned Wallings ice cream. A collection of craft beers, ales and ciders provide further reason to hang out for a while.

If it's busy downstairs, make for the roomy first floor space with its comfy armchairs where you're bound to find a spot in which to spread out.

ESTABLISHED
2015

KEY ROASTER
Atkinsons
Coffee Roasters

BREWING METHOD
Espresso, V60,
cold brew,
cafetiere,
Clever Dripper

MACHINE
Sanremo Verona

GRINDER
Sanremo

OPENING HOURS
Mon-Sat 10am-6pm
Sun 11am-5pm
(seasonal opening hours)

BEANS AVAILABLE
INSTORE

WIFI

OUTDOOR SEATING

BRING YOUR OWN CUP

www.cedarwood.coffee   T: 01772 821769

f @cedarwoodcoffee   🐦 @winckleystreet   📷 @cedarwoodcoffee

MAP №15 EXCHANGE COFFEE COMPANY – BLACKBURN

13-15 Fleming Square, Blackburn, Lancashire, BB2 2DG

If you're a sucker for the smell of freshly roasted coffee, you'll be powerless to resist the aromas emanating from Exchange Arcade in the heart of Blackburn. Step a little closer and, behind the impressive Victorian facade, you'll find Exchange Coffee's Probat LN12 roasting beans daily.

The freshness of the brew is complemented by the quality of the beans, some sourced directly from four small Brazilian coffee farms that are both Rainforest Alliance and UTZ certified. Such commitment to the caffeine cause may well explain Exchange's impressive accumulation of 40 Great Taste awards.

INSIDER'S tip NO ROOM AT THE INN? THE GUYS ALSO HAVE A COFFEE BAR IN BLACKBURN MARKET

Having chosen your bean and serve style – espresso, french press or Clever Dripper are available – you can opt to sip it amid oak panelling and William Morris wallpaper on the ground floor, head upstairs to watch clouds skimming by above the glass roof or go next door to the dog-friendly 1849 private dining room.

Those keen to fuel up for the day shouldn't pass on the full Lancashire breakfast, while refined afternoon teas come served on prettily patterned Burleigh Ware.

ESTABLISHED
1986

KEY ROASTER
Exchange Coffee Company

BREWING METHOD
Espresso, Clever Dripper, french press

MACHINE
Cimbali M34

GRINDER
Mahlkonig K30, Ditting KR804

OPENING HOURS
Mon-Sat 9am-5.30pm

www.exchangecoffee.co.uk T: 01254 54258
f @exchangecoffeecompany @exchange_coffee @exchange_coffee

№16 SIPHON ESPRESSO & BREW BAR

91 Bank Street, Rawtenstall, Rossendale, Lancashire, BB4 7QN

This Rawtenstall indie fits all the criteria for wish-it-was-at-the-bottom-of-my-road status: mind-bogglingly good beans? Check. Multiple brewing methods to match your mood? Check. Laid-back, feel-good vibes? Full house.

It's no surprise that locals flock to Scott Moore's espresso and brew bar for their daily fix of quality caffeine. There are plenty of options for them to choose from: Manchester's Ancoats beans are the regular attraction on the Sanremo espresso machine, while regional guests including Crosby, Neighbourhood and Grindsmith take turns on filter. Chilled cans of Minor Figures nitro cold brew are also on hand for hot days.

INSIDE'S TIP DON'T LEAVE WITHOUT PICKING UP A LOAF OF TROVE SOURDOUGH

While the focus at Siphon is mostly on coffee, it would be difficult not to appreciate a side order of toasted banana bread topped with a healthy dollop of mascarpone and sprinkle of blueberries.

A counter of homemade bakes (try and resist an Oreo brownie) provides additional sugar highs and coffee pairing potential.

ESTABLISHED
2018

KEY ROASTER
Ancoats Coffee Co.

BREWING METHOD
Espresso,
syphon,
cold brew

MACHINE
Sanremo
Verona RS

GRINDER
Eureka Mythos,
Mazzer Mini

OPENING HOURS
Mon-Fri
7.30am-5.30pm
Sat 8.30am-5.30pm
Sun 8.30am-5pm

T: 07740 366167

f @siphonespressobrewbar 🐦 @siphonespresso1 📷 @siphonespressobrewbar

— MANCHESTER —
COFFEE
FESTIVAL

BACK
FOR
2020

TALKS
TASTING
BREWING
ROASTERS
WORKSHOPS
COMPETITIONS

@CUPNORTH

MAP № 17 CROSBY COFFEE

2 Oxford Road, Waterloo, Liverpool, Merseyside, L22 8QF

Crosby Coffee has a foolproof plan: source exquisite beans, roast them meticulously at its roastery, then deliver them next door where baristas turn them into espresso based drinks and filter brews for Crosby's loyal band of followers.

If it's coffee related, these guys do it. Brewing methods include Chemex, V60 and nitro cold brew. And, if you're not sure what to order, the baristas (fully accredited by the Specialty Coffee Association) are always happy to advise.

INSIDER'S tip HAVE LUNCH AND A BREW IN THE CAFE THEN TAKE A NOSY NEXT DOOR AT THE ROASTERY

Batch brew is a new addition at the flagship cafe and is crafted from single origin beans (rotated monthly) to deliver an unfussy filter option which doesn't scrimp on breadth of flavour. Three grinders are on permanent duty to keep the blends, singles and decaf a-coming.

Crosby's newly refurbed training room further proves commitment to the caffeine cause. If you love the cup you get in the cafe, you can learn how to recreate it at home at one of the regular public sessions. In need of some kit? That's available, too.

ESTABLISHED
2017

KEY ROASTER
Crosby Coffee

BREWING METHOD
Espresso, V60 batch brew, Chemex, nitro

MACHINE
Conti Monte Carlo

GRINDER
Compak E6, Compak E8, Mahlkonig EK43

OPENING HOURS
Mon-Fri 8am-4.30pm
Sat 9am-4pm
Sun 10am-3pm

Gluten FREE

BEANS AVAILABLE
INSTORE

WIFI

CYCLE FRIENDLY

OUTDOOR seating

DISABLED ACCESS

BRING YOUR OWN Cup

COFFEE COURSES

DOG FRIENDLY

---

www.crosbycoffee.co.uk   T: 01515 385454

f @crosbycoffee   🐦 @coffeecrosby   📷 @crosbycoffeeltd

MAP № 18 ROOT COFFEE

52 Hanover Street, Liverpool, Merseyside, L1 4AF

If you like to mix up coffee serve styles and love trying new beans, it's worth folding the corner of this page down.

Enthused and inspired by coffee festival culture, the Root team sought to recreate the thrill of tasting lots of different coffees via a multitude of kit when they launched their Liverpool coffee shop in 2015. As a result, the coffee bill features a roster of different roasters, while the armoury of brewing paraphernalia is always well stocked.

INSIDER'S TIP VISIT FOR A LATE-AFTERNOON NITRO ESPRESSO MARTINI

Craft House, Hard Beans, Casino Mocca and Round Hill are all recent favourites, though the line-up of roasters changes on an almost weekly basis. If you're unfamiliar with Root's latest star beans, the baristas are friendly and always up for talking through the tasting notes.

The food offering is pretty great too – don't miss house faves such as banana and Nutella pancakes or mixed bean and avo bagels.

This central spot is spacious and airy, so bring a book or your laptop and kick back for a couple of hours.

ESTABLISHED
2015

KEY ROASTER
Multiple roasters

BREWING METHOD
Espresso, Chemex, cold brew, V60

MACHINE
Victoria Arduino Black Eagle Gravimetric

GRINDER
Mythos One, Mythos Two, Mahlkonig Peak, Mahlkonig EK43

OPENING HOURS
Mon-Sat
8.30am-6.30pm
Sun 9am-6pm

Gluten FREE

BEANS AVAILABLE
INSTORE

WIFI

CYCLE FRIENDLY

OUTDOOR SEATING

DISABLED ACCESS

BRING YOUR OWN Cup

COFFEE COURSES

DOG FRIENDLY

www.rootcoffee.co.uk

f @rootcoffeeliv   🐦 @rootcoffeeliv   📷 @rootcoffeeliv

№19 ROPES AND TWINES

70 Bold Street, Liverpool, Merseyside, L1 4HR

opes and Twines does a sterling job of combining two of life's greatest pleasures (coffee and wine) within one of Liverpool's slickest venues.

In case you were wondering what rope or twine has to do with either, it's named after its location in Ropewalks, an area of the city known for rope making in the 19th century.

While the main draws are speciality grade coffee and carefully selected bottles of wine, a busy schedule of live music events and a photography gallery attract a wide range of creatives to the Bold Street shop.

INSIDER'S TIP POP IN FOR ONE OF THE REGULAR WINE TASTING EVENTS

A vast bar runs the whole length of the white walled, minimalist space and features a slick inbuilt Mavam machine. Leeds roastery Maude takes the main spot on the coffee bill and is often joined by guests such as Five Elephant, Outpost and Craft House.

Order a V60 and wedge of glossy cheesecake and head to the window seats for the pick of the people-watching spots.

ESTABLISHED
2018

KEY ROASTER
Maude Coffee
Roasters

BREWING METHOD
Espresso, V60

MACHINE
Mavam

GRINDER
Mythos One

OPENING HOURS
Mon-Thu **8**am-**7**pm
Fri **8**am-**11**pm
Sat **9.30**am-**11**pm
Sun **9.30**am-**6**pm

WIFI

www.ropes-and-twines.co.uk

f @ropesandtwines @ropesandtwines

№ 20 BOLD STREET COFFEE

89 Bold Street, Liverpool, Merseyside, L1 4HF

While Sam Tawil's Liverpool coffee shop has been on the hit list of every clued-up speciality fan since 2010, a recent refit has also put Bold Street on the radar of the city's epicurean contingent.

A new open kitchen and reshuffle of the cafe space has allowed Sam and team to expand their menu and extend the opening hours to include evening service from Thursday to Sunday. Locals can now drop in for post-work drinks and dishes such as coffee-braised beef with crispy polenta and blistered vine tomatoes.

Brunch is also big business at Bold Street and, with a new dining space downstairs, there's even more room in which to chow down on maple and bacon pancakes or creamy wild mushrooms on toast (with a side order of mellow beats from the vinyl-inspired playlist).

INSIDER'S TIP — BOLD STREET IS A THREE-TIME WINNER OF THE BEST COFFEE SHOP IN LIVERPOOL GONG

That said, quality coffee is still the main focus. The gang keep things fresh behind the bar, changing the Hasbean single origin on espresso every month and guesting roasters such as Round Hill on filter.

ESTABLISHED
2010

KEY ROASTER
Hasbean

BREWING METHOD
Espresso,
AeroPress,
Chemex,
batch brew

MACHINE
La Marzocco
Linea PB

GRINDER
Nuova Simonelli
Mythos One,
Nuova Simonelli
Mythos II,
Mahlkonig EK43

OPENING HOURS
Mon-Fri 7.30am-8pm
Sat 8am-8pm
Sun 9am-8pm

Gluten FREE

BEANS AVAILABLE INSTORE

WIFI

CYCLE FRIENDLY

DISABLED ACCESS

BRING YOUR OWN Cup

DOG FRIENDLY

---

www.boldstreetcoffee.co.uk   T: 01517 097172

f @bold.street.coffee   🐦 @boldstcoffee   📷 @boldstreetcoffee

MAP No. 21 92 DEGREES

36 Myrtle Street, Liverpool, Merseyside, L7 7AP

92 Degrees has been a trailblazer on the Liverpool coffee scene since it opened its first cafe in 2015.

This latest outpost in the roastery's clutch of three is a contemporary corner cafe on Myrtle Street, where the team build on 92's reputation for cracking caffeine and friendly vibes.

INSIDER'S TIP — DOWNLOAD THE 92 DEGREES APP TO COLLECT LOYALTY POINTS FOR YOUR BREWS

The new site gets its beans fresh from the Baltic Roastery in the city's bustling creative quarter, where the greens are roasted on a trusty 6kg Giesen. The baristas know the latest batches inside and out and are happy to share the backstory of each of the single origins on offer at the brew bar. They're also keen to spread the word about the social and environmental work the roastery has been getting involved in recently.

Whether you choose the Hope Street house blend or sample something fruity on filter, pair your pick with a wicked brownie slab from the counter. If you're practising a plant-based diet, you'll like the killer collection of locally crafted vegan and gluten-free bakes.

ESTABLISHED
2015

KEY ROASTER
92 Degrees Coffee

BREWING METHOD
Espresso, V60, cold brew

MACHINE
Faema E71E

GRINDER
Mazzer Kold

OPENING HOURS
Mon-Fri **8**am-**6**pm
Sat **10**am-**6**pm
Sun **10**am-**5**pm

Gluten FREE

BEANS AVAILABLE
INSTORE

WIFI

CYCLE FRIENDLY

OUTDOOR Seating

DISABLED ACCESS

BRING YOUR OWN Cup

COFFEE COURSES

DOG FRIENDLY

---

www.92degreescoffee.com   T: 01517 091145
f @92degreescoffee   🐦 @92degreescoffee   📷 @92degreescoffee

MAP №22 BEAN THERE COFFEE SHOP

376 Smithdown Road, Liverpool, Merseyside, L15 5AN

This south Liverpool favourite features guest roasts from across the UK plus a wide variety of filter kit, yet its eclectic range of regulars (yoga mums, local knitting groups, laptop warriors and students) prove that speciality coffee doesn't need to be niche.

The cafe's location on the corner of Penny Lane also makes it a must-visit for Beatles fans who stop off for cappuccino and cake on their magical mystery tour of the city.

INSIDE'S tip ONE SHOT TOO MANY? SINK A RESTORATIVE BLENDSMITHS BEETROOT LATTE

Founder Andrew Mulligan ensures that there is always a good selection of coffees to choose from and features a house roast from Atkinsons in Lancaster, alongside local roasters Neighbourhood and far-flung indies like Horsham.

The homemade fodder is another draw. Freshly made sausage rolls stuffed with 24-hour-cooked pork and Bramley apple are an obvious choice, as is the veggie version which features harissa-spiced cauliflower, feta and pomegranate. Or, make like a local and order the salt and pepper chicken burger stack.

ESTABLISHED
2017

KEY ROASTER
Atkinsons
Coffee Roasters

BREWING METHOD
Espresso, V60,
Chemex,
batch brew,
cold brew

MACHINE
La Marzocco
Linea PB

GRINDER
Mythos One
Clima Pro,
Mahlkonig EK43

OPENING HOURS
Mon-Fri **7.30**am-**7**pm
Sat-Sun **9**am-**5**pm

www.beantherecoffeeshop.com   T: 01517 332324

f @beantherecoffeeshop   🐦 @beanthere_lpl   📷 @beantherecoffeeshop

MAP № 23 CAFFÈ & CO.

8 Dane Court, Rainhill, Prescot, Merseyside, L35 4LU

Whatever the time of day, however strong your caffeine craving and no matter the size of your appetite, this friendly village cafe can satiate your need for lip-smackingly good coffee and scrumptious goodies.

Kickstart the day with a smooth flat white and a freshly baked croissant, bacon butty or trad full English brekkie. Come mid-morning, a crema-rich shot of espresso – courtesy of Curious Roo's Barn Door blend – is the perfect accompaniment to Belgian waffles and French crepes.

INSIDER'S TIP — GEN UP VIA CUPPINGS AND COURSES AT THE SCA TRAINING SCHOOL UPSTAIRS

Then, at midday, sandwiches, baguettes, panini and salads (many vegan friendly) satisfy rumbling tums, especially when followed by homemade ice cream or sorbet (there are more than 80 fantastical flavours to choose from).

For further adventures in coffee, take the opportunity to explore distinctive flavours on filter from monthly changing guests like Union Roasted and Gardelli.

ESTABLISHED
2011

KEY ROASTER
Curious Roo
Coffee Roasters

BREWING METHOD
Espresso,
AeroPress,
Clever Dripper,
french press,
V60

MACHINE
La Marzocco GB5

GRINDER
Victoria Arduino
Mythos One

OPENING HOURS
Mon-Sat 8am-5pm
Sun 9am-3pm

Gluten FREE

BEANS AVAILABLE
INSTORE

WIFI

CYCLE FRIENDLY

OUTDOOR seating

DISABLED ACCESS

BRING YOUR OWN Cup

COFFEE COURSES

---

www.caffeandco.com   T: 01514 932332

f @caffeandco   🐦 @caffeandco   📷 @caffe_and_co

Coffee
FRE
BREW
CAPPUCCINO · LAT
am · milk · suga
DARK
ROAST
ESPRESSO

ROASTERS

№29
Kircabi Roasters

24 CARVETII COFFEE ROASTERS

Threlkeld Business Park, Threlkeld, Cumbria, CA12 4SU

The Carvetii crew are obsessed with coffee, which means constantly learning new stuff and passing on that knowledge in the manner of true caffeine evangelists.

Having 25kg and 12kg Probat roasters at HQ means there is capacity to have six coffees on rotation at any one time, and Carvetii's customers are kept well supplied with a seasonal espresso blend, a (less acidic) Knott Halloo blend, three single origins for filter and a decaf option.

'THE TECHNICALITIES OF ROASTING THE BEANS ARE TREATED AS BOTH AN ART AND A SCIENCE'

The guys scour the world's coffee growing regions for choice beans and make a point of knowing as much about the farmers and growing conditions as possible. Lots for blending are sympathetically and expertly selected, while the technicalities of roasting the beans are treated as both an art and a science.

In addition to keeping its cafe customers buzzing with just-out-of-the-roaster beans, Carvetii also delivers expert training to ensure every brew is spot-on. And 24/7 technical support doesn't go amiss, either.

ESTABLISHED
2011

ROASTER
MAKE v. SIZE
Probatone 25kg
Probat UC12 12kg

www.carvetiicoffee.co.uk   01768 776979

@carvetiicoffee   @carvetiicoffee   @carvetiicoffee

25 RED BANK COFFEE ROASTERS

Unit 3a, Lake Road Estate, Lake Road, Coniston, Cumbria, LA21 8EW

It's been another big year for the team at Red Bank Coffee Roasters in Cumbria.

The acquisition of a slick Loring S15 Falcon roaster has enabled the gang to meet the increasing demand for their coffee and unlock every last drop of flavour from the greens, while also improving the roastery's carbon footprint.

Sustainability has always been a priority for the team: the roastery's electricity is supplied by 100 per cent renewable sources, a recycling scheme allows customers to return coffee bags, and long-term relationships with farmers ensure ethical trading.

Red Bank's continued focus on quality, traceability and sustainability has helped the indie gain greater recognition within the speciality scene this year, with venues across the North and beyond filling their grinders with its Lake District-roasted beans.

A FOCUS ON QUALITY, TRACEABILITY AND SUSTAINABILITY

The roastery's latest release is a collaboration with Wonderful Wild Women, a Lakes community project which encourages women to get outdoors regardless of their age or experience.

ESTABLISHED
2015

ROASTER
MAKE & SIZE
Loring 15kg
Giesen 6kg

BEANS
AVAILABLE
ONLINE

www.redbankcoffee.com   07850 291171
@redbankcoffee

26 MR DUFFINS COFFEE

49 Main Street, Staveley, Kendal, Cumbria, LA8 9LN

Starting out in 2014 with a domestic roaster intended for a bit of kitchen experimentation, Steven Duffin was seduced by the craft of coffee roasting and before long had upgraded to a 2kg Brazilian model.

What followed were trial-and-error sessions and late-night eBay purchases which eventually led to the launch of a full-blown roastery and the acquisition of the majestic 15kg Giesen that now resides at the Staveley HQ.

A small batch and regular roasting schedule allows Steven to fire up the Giesen multiple times a week, while also guaranteeing optimum freshness for the bevy of Cumbrian cafes he supplies.

ESTABLISHED
2014

ROASTER
Giesen 15kg

'VISITORS CAN WATCH THE MAGIC HAPPEN AT THE ROASTERY CAFE'

Fans of Mr Duffins' jet-setting collection of beans can watch the magic happen at the roastery cafe The Coffee Den. And, while the Giesen gently bronzes the next batch of Peruvian greens (sustainably sourced to support indigenous tribes), visitors can sip a flat white while nibbling a chunk of homemade espresso fudge.

www.mrduffinscoffee.com   01539 822192

@mrduffins   @mrduffins   @mr.duffins.coffee

27 RINALDO'S SPECIALTY COFFEE & FINE TEA

Unit 12, Lakeland Food Park (Plumgarths), Kendal, Cumbria, LA8 8QJ

After bringing speciality beans to the people of Cumbria via his mobile coffee van, Rin Colombi crowdfunded his way to a permanent roastery in 2015.

Two years later, he found a new home at Lakeland Food Park, a move that enabled him to build an espresso bar and training centre alongside the roasting equipment.

NIFTY NEW PLASTIC-AND-FOIL-FREE PACKAGING CAN BE RETURNED FOR REFILLING

While you *can* order online, it's hard to beat swinging by to sample the Casa house blend or one of the variety seasonal single origins on-site. It's worth noting that this is a take-out-only situation, so pack your KeepCup. If you forget, it's not game over as Rin stocks a selection alongside brewing paraphernalia and beans in nifty new plastic-and-foil-free packaging which can be returned to the roastery for refilling (plus a discount).

ESTABLISHED
2015

ROASTER
MAKE & SIZE
Giesen W15A
15kg

www.rinscoffee.com   01539 592587

@rinscoffee   @rinscoffee   @rinscoffee

28 FARRER'S TEA & COFFEE

9 Shap Road Industrial Estate, Kendal, Cumbria, LA9 6NZ

It's fair to say that Farrer's has experience on its side. The roastery opened in 1819 (the year of Queen Victoria's birth) and is celebrating 200 years in the business, making it one of the oldest surviving coffee roasters in the UK.

Its team are also well seasoned and include four dedicated roasters with more than six decades of specialist knowledge between them. And, while it is impossible to fake this kind of heritage or learn overnight what these guys know about coffee, Farrer's is not all about basking in past glories.

'FOUR DEDICATED ROASTERS HAVE MORE THAN SIX DECADES OF SPECIALIST KNOWLEDGE BETWEEN THEM'

Today, the pioneering roastery produces over 50 blends and single origin coffees with responsibly sourced beans from across the growing belt.

It kicked off its bicentenary year with a visit from HRH Countess of Wessex and is embracing new-found eco practices, including the introduction of recyclable aluminium pods, and beans sealed in recyclable tins and coffee bags.

ESTABLISHED
1819

ROASTER
MAKE & SIZE
Probat G60 60kg
Vittoria 15kg
Probatino 1.5kg x 2

www.farrerscoffee.co.uk   01539 720020

@farrersteaandcoffee   @farrers_coffee   @farrersteaandcoffee

29 KIRCABI ROASTERS

The Royal Barn, New Road, Kirkby Lonsdale, Cumbria, LA6 2AB

The talented team at Kircabi fully embrace the indie spirit of producing incredible craft drinks and, in addition to roasting ethically traded green beans, brew unique cask ales and serve them at their on-site tap room, Royal Barn.

Sourcing and roasting unique blends and single origin coffees for local brands, coffee houses and businesses is another strand of the set-up. Visitors can witness all of this incredible multitasking on a roastery tour which finishes at the in-house cafe with a chance to sample the latest batch on filter.

'EACH BAG FEATURES ADDITIONAL NOTES ON THE FARMER'

Fans who order Kirkby Lonsdale-roasted beans online to brew at home are treated to an extra shot of coffee knowledge as each bag features notes on the growing region and the farmers who cultivated the crop.

'If you're anything like us, you'll want to know exactly where your coffee comes from. That's why every cup of sustainable Kircabi coffee tells its own unique story,' says founder Stu Taylor.

ESTABLISHED
2016

ROASTER
MAKE & SIZE
Toper 5kg

www.kircabiroasters.co.uk   01524 271918

@kircabi   @kircabiroasters   @kircabiroasters

12 China Street, Lancaster, Lancashire, LA1 1EX

While some roasters comb every inch of the coffee growing belt to offer a jet-setting selection of origins, Atkinsons founder Ian Steel prefers to focus his attention on a small number of farms.

'Our preference is to work with fewer producers but to delve deeper to unearth undiscovered gems,' he explains.

Building long-lasting relationships with these farmers is high on the Atkinsons agenda, and Ian and the team make regular trips to origin to meet growers and glean on-the-ground intel on the best beans. Recent visits have resulted in a collection of relationship coffees which includes an anaerobically fermented Brazilian micro-lot.

"REGULAR TRIPS TO ORIGIN GLEAN ON-THE-GROUND INTEL ON THE BEST BEANS"

Beyond the roastery, the Atkinsons empire has continued to expand (you'll find two cafes in Lancaster and another at Manchester's Mackie Mayor) and a fourth venue is due to open in Lancaster Castle in late 2019. The newly refurbished wing within the 11th century landmark will serve the roastery's award winning coffees alongside a menu of savouries and cakes baked at flagship cafe The Hall.

ESTABLISHED
1837

ROASTER
MAKE & SIZE
Loring Kestrel 35kg
Whitmee 56lb
Whitmee 28lb
Uno 14lb
Uno 7lb

CAFE ONSITE

OPEN BY APPOINTMENT

COFFEE COURSES

BEANS AVAILABLE

www.thecoffeehopper.com   01524 65470

@atkinsonscoffee   @coffeehopper   @atkinsons.coffee

Nº16
Siphon Espresso & Brew Bar

31 EXCHANGE COFFEE COMPANY

The Old Baptist Chapel, Islington, Canterbury Street, Blackburn, Lancashire, BB2 2LN

A holy trinity of roasters (a pair of Petroncini and a Probat, to be precise) are the tools with which the roasters at Exchange create heavenly coffee experiences.

Single estate and micro-lot beans (which have won 40 Great Taste awards between them) are roasted to divine perfection at this roastery housed in a former baptist chapel. The adjoining barista training centre where students congregate to learn the creeds of great caffeine is where the Sunday school used to be held.

The roasters cook up a portfolio of coffees from 15 countries and recently began trading directly with four small Brazilian farms (Rainforest Alliance and UTZ certified), ensuring fair prices are paid to the farmers.

'LOOK OUT FOR THE NEW DELIVERY VANS POWERED BY SOLAR PANELS'

Exchange also supports baristas by installing and maintaining Cimbali and Expobar espresso machines at customers' venues across the region.

Pay homage to the beans yourself at the roasting shop in Fleming Square and the coffee bar in Blackburn Market. And look out for the two new delivery vans – powered by the solar panels on the chapel roof.

ESTABLISHED
1996

ROASTER
MAKE & SIZE
Petroncini TTA
60 60kg

Probat GN25
25kg

Petroncini TTA
15/20 20kg

OPEN
BY APPOINTMENT

COFFEE
COURSES

BEANS
AVAILABLE

www.exchangecoffee.co.uk   01254 781560

@exchangecoffeecompany   @exchange_coffee   @exchange_coffee

32 ROBERTS & CO.

Cedar Farm, Back Lane, Mawdesley, Ormskirk, Lancashire, L40 3SY

Working together to create award winning teas and speciality grade coffees is a time-honoured tradition for the Roberts clan: the family have spent over a century sourcing green beans and tea leaves from around the globe.

The business has come a long way since its inception in the 1890s. Today you'll find Roberts & Co. HQ at Cedar Farm, a converted pig barn in the Lancashire wilds which is a hub for artists and local producers.

ESTABLISHED
1891

ROASTER MAKE & SIZE
Vintage Whitmee 20kg

Vintage Whitmee 6kg

CAFE ONSITE

BEANS AVAILABLE

> "THE FAMILY HAVE SPENT OVER A CENTURY SOURCING GREEN BEANS"

The Roberts team roast their sustainably sourced green beans on two vintage Whitmee flame roasters, and the coffee can be sampled at the Roberts espresso bar. Try a bespoke blend such as Espresso Siena which delivers a silky mouthfeel, or plump for a single origin.

There's a huge selection of coffees and teas for visitors to choose from and the caffeinated offering is fortified by homemade cakes and veggie eats.

www.e-coffee.co.uk   01704 822433

@Roberts & Co Roastery   @robertsco_coffee

№33 DJANGO COFFEE CO.

24 Kenilworth Road, Ainsdale, Southport, Merseyside, PR8 3PE

After half a decade of globetrotting and time spent in Melbourne's inspirational speciality scene, Ste Paweleck felt galvanised to set up his own roastery. The result was Django Coffee, a tribute to the people Ste met and the cultures he encountered while travelling through coffee-producing regions.

ESTABLISHED
2016

ROASTER
MAKE & SIZE
Giesen W6A 6kg

BEANS
AVAILABLE

'SUSTAINABILITY IS IMPORTANT TO PRODUCE QUALITY COFFEE'

The eco-conscious small-batch roastery is focused on direct trade and single origins, and Ste's ethics permeate so that everything is executed in a way that does justice to the planet and the farmers who've grown the crop.

'Sustainability is important to produce quality coffee, livelihood longevity and a healthy environment,' he says. *'Working directly with local producers or companies helps farmers with finance and education, and improves sustainable farming techniques.'*

This year Ste travelled to Guatemala to source and import coffees which will take their turn in the Giesen alongside greens garnered – via trusted suppliers – directly from farms and co-operatives.

www.djangocoffeeco.com 07490 387610

@djangocoffeeco   @djangocoffee   @djangocoffeeco

34 CROSBY COFFEE

2 Oxford Road, Waterloo, Liverpool, Merseyside, L22 8QF

The Crosby crew have roasted speciality grade beans in Liverpool since 2014, but last year went next-level when they expanded to a huge new distribution hub.

The roomier digs (just down the road from the roastery cafe in Waterloo) have allowed the team to bolster the roasting operation and scale up their nationwide subscription service.

A PERSONALISED BAG OF CROSBY BEANS GUARANTEES BROWNIE POINTS

Green beans for the three house blends and selection of single origins are largely sourced from South and Central America, though micro-lots such as an Ethiopian Yirgacheffe often make seasonal appearances on the online shop and in the monthly subscriptions.

If you're looking for a unique present for your favourite coffee geek, a personalised bag of Crosby beans guarantees brownie points. For wholesale customers, the crew offer machine rentals, comprehensive barista training, alt milks and more.

ESTABLISHED
2014

ROASTER
MAKE & SIZE
Toper 30kg
Toper 10kg

CAFE ONSITE

OPEN
BY APPOINTMENT

COFFEE COURSES

BEANS AVAILABLE

www.crosbycoffee.co.uk | 01515 385454

@crosbycoffee | @coffeecrosby | @crosbycoffeeltd

35 NEIGHBOURHOOD COFFEE

Unit 89, Chadwick Court, Chadwick Street, Liverpool, Merseyside, L3 7EY

It's been a chocka year of caffeinated adventures for Liverpool's Neighbourhood roastery team.
In addition to a shiny new rebrand and winning three Great Taste awards, the team also took trips to Brazil and Colombia.

The aim was to build even stronger bonds with the coffee-growing communities and source flavour-popping small batches to bring home and cook up on the Giesen W15A. The trips were such a success that the team even secured a new sourcing relationship with a co-operative in Colombia which resulted in bagging a supply of world-exclusive micro-lots.

'BAGGING A SUPPLY OF WORLD-EXCLUSIVE MICRO-LOTS'

The guys have also recently launched their first cafe (Framework Coffee), which is the go-to spot for tasting these ethically sourced Neighbourhood beans and taking part in home barista courses.

To keep up with the daily grind, the team have expanded and welcomed two new bean brains to the fold.

ESTABLISHED
2014

ROASTED
MAKE & SIZE
Giesen W15A
15kg

www.neighbourhoodcoffee.co.uk   01512 366741

@neighbourhoodcoffee   @nhoodcoffee   @neighbourhoodcoffee

36 92 DEGREES AND THE BALTIC ROASTERY

49 Jamaica Street, Liverpool, Merseyside, L1 0AH

The intoxicating aroma of straight-from-the-drum coffee lures bean geeks, students, flagging tourists and local business folk into Liverpool's first roastery coffee shop.

With an on-site brew bar and three other venues in the North West to keep stocked with ethically sourced beans, the Baltic team find themselves roasting up to five times a week.

"THE INTOXICATING AROMA LURES BEAN GEEKS INTO LIVERPOOL'S FIRST ROASTERY COFFEE SHOP"

An ethical cup is important to the gang and they know the links in the supply chain as names not numbers. A percentage of retail sales goes to Project Waterfall which works to improve coffee farmers' access to clean drinking water.

Sample the latest blends and single origins at one of the regular cupping sessions or order a bag online to road-test at home. A good place to start is the house espresso, Hope Street, which offers notes of salted caramel, dark chocolate and blueberry.

ESTABLISHED
2015

ROASTER
MAKE & SIZE
Giesen W6E

CAFE ONSITE

BEANS AVAILABLE

www.92degreescoffee.com

@92degreescoffee @92degreescoffee @92degreescoffee

MAP № 37 CAFFÈ & CO.

8 Dane Court, Rainhill, Prescot, Merseyside, L35 4LU

Whether you're a shot puller looking to brush up your barista skills, a coffee-preneur wanting to open a cafe or a home brewer who cares about the quality of your morning cup, there's a course at this training space and coffee shop.

Owner Neil Osthoff, an SCA diploma graduate who has schooled baristas in the art of coffee at his Rainhill cafe since 2011, offers accredited diplomas in barista, brewing and sensory courses. He says: *'SCA accreditation gives a new coffee shop owner considerable recognition. It shows you're serious about coffee and that you'll be following certain principles and procedures.'*

'SCA ACCREDITATION GIVES A NEW BUSINESS OWNER CONSIDERABLE RECOGNITION'

You don't need to be a cafe owner to visit the lab for cupping and tasting sessions however. All kinds of coffee fans are welcomed to the classes which are kept small to ensure everyone gets their turn on kit like the new La Marzocco Linea Mini, Linea PB, Mythos and EK43.

ESTABLISHED
2011

CAFE ONSITE

COFFEE COURSES

SPECIALTY COFFEE ASSOCIATION COURSES

BEANS AVAILABLE ONSITE

---

www.caffeandco.com   **T:** 01514 932332

f @caffeandco   🐦 @caffeandco   📷 @caffe_and_co

NORTH WALES

№45
Dyfi Roastery

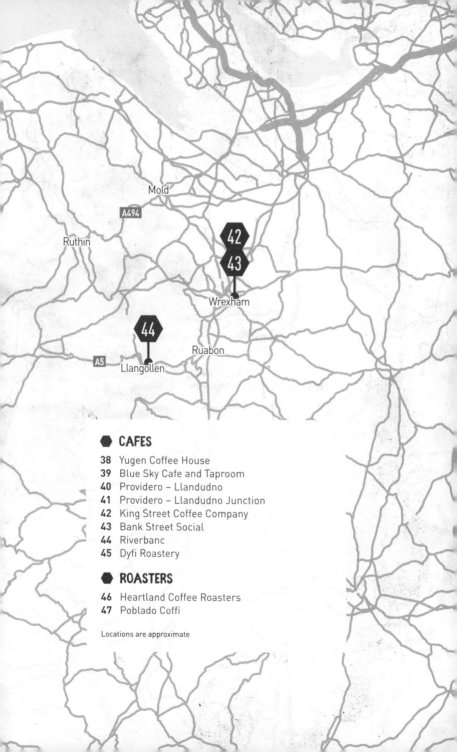

CAFES

ROASTERS

Locations are approximate

MAP 38 YUGEN COFFEE HOUSE

Unit 16, Menai Shopping Centre, Garth Road, Bangor, Gwynedd, Wales, LL57 1DN

The Japanese concept of Yugen alludes to moments that are so profoundly beautiful they can't be summed up in words. A tall order indeed for a coffee shop and cafe, but one worth striving for.

Taking a bit of 'me time' is a handy hack for channelling a more blissed-out mindset, and the relaxed surroundings at Yugen (many regulars treat it as their second home) encourage visitors to do just that.

Savour each sip of Allpress coffee served as espresso or filter, or dally over delicious alternatives such as hot or iced beetroot, matcha, turmeric and chai latte.

INSIDER'S tip GET A 10P DISCOUNT WHEN YOU USE YOUR KEEPCUP FOR A TAKEAWAY BREW

Owner Gavin Lin aims to serve only the best, and this includes the menu of vegan and veggie brunches crafted from ultra-fresh local ingredients.

For a moment worth cherishing, the falafel panini or a couple of slices of local thick-cut toast laden with butter and jam will have you feeling pretty zen.

ESTABLISHED
2018

KEY ROASTER
Allpress Espresso

BREWING METHOD
Espresso, AeroPress

MACHINE
La Marzocco Linea Classic

GRINDER
Mazzer Luigi

OPENING HOURS
Mon-Sat 8.30am-4pm

www.yugencoffeehouse.com

f @yugencoffeehouse @yugencoffeehouse

MAP N° 39 BLUE SKY CAFE AND TAPROOM

Ambassadors Hall, rear of 236 High Street, Bangor, Gwynedd, Wales, LL57 1PA

If you're in any doubt that the speciality coffee and indie beer scenes are booming in North Wales, you should schedule a trip to this cathedral to the crafts.

From its former warehouse (and second world war dancehall) setting, Blue Sky curates beans and brews from the region's finest roasteries and breweries. The line-up is seriously impressive and there are up to 15 coffees and over 100 different beers available at any time.

Five grinders, two espresso machines and a trusty Moccamaster take care of the revolving selection of beans from local roasters Heartland, Poblado, Dragon and Eryri. And the mix of blends, single origins and decafs means the baristas can usually find a good match for each individual customer's preference.

INSIDER'S TIP THE 2018 REFURB HAS RESULTED IN STACKS OF SPACE, SO FEEL FREE TO HANG AROUND

If Blue Sky didn't have enough going for it, the kitchen has also scored the cafe a place in the *Good Food Guide* eight times. Dedicated vegan and meat chefs ensure the bill of sarnies, burgers and specials caters to everyone.

ESTABLISHED
2009

KEY ROASTER
Poblado Coffi

BREWING METHOD
Espresso,
AeroPress,
Moccamaster

MACHINE
La Spaziale S5,
La Marzocco
Linea Classic

GRINDER
Mahlkonig EK43,
Victoria Arduino
Mythos One,
Anfim SCODY,
Mazzer Super

OPENING HOURS
Mon-Thu 9.30am-10pm
Fri 9.30am-11pm
Sat 9.30am-12am

Gluten FREE

BEANS AVAILABLE INSTORE

WIFI

DISABLED ACCESS

BRING YOUR OWN Cup

www.blueskybangor.co.uk   T: 01248 355444

f @blueskybangor   🐦 @blueskybangor   📷 @blueskycafebangor

MAP Nº 40 PROVIDERO – LLANDUDNO

112 Upper Mostyn Street, Llandudno, Conwy, Wales, LL30 2SW

Road tripping across North Wales? Once you've sunk a punchy espresso at the original Providero at Llandudno Junction, you'll want to call in at this sister venue for the full food and drink experience.

The second cafe to be crowdsourced by Prov founder Jon Hughes, this site builds on the original with a fattened food menu, more seating and a busy calendar of book launches, coffee tastings and live music events. There's even a baby grand piano for impromptu performances by the cafe's more musical patrons.

INSIDER'S tip HUNKER DOWN IN THE COSY SNUG WITH A BOWL OF HONEY-DRIZZLED CREAMY PORRIDGE

Down-the-road roastery Heartland supplies Wales' first Sanremo Opera machine with a stellar house blend and a selection of single origin and single estate coffees. Jon and the Prov family also enjoy discovering new beans while on their travels and often bring them back to the brew bar to share with customers.

A creative kitchen team round out the experience with healthy, seasonal brunch dishes which demonstrate how exciting (and delicious) veggie cafe cooking can be.

ESTABLISHED
2017

KEY ROASTER
Heartland
Coffee Roasters

BREWING METHOD
Espresso,
AeroPress,
Clever Dripper,
batch brew

MACHINE
Sanremo Opera

GRINDER
Mythos One
Clima Pro,
Mahlkonig EK43

OPENING HOURS
Mon-Sat 8am-6pm
Sun 9am-5pm

---

www.providero.co.uk   T: 01492 338220

f @providero   🐦 @providero   📷 @providero.tea.coffee

MAP №41 PROVIDERO – LLANDUDNO JUNCTION

148 Conway Road, Llandudno Junction, Conwy, Wales, LL31 9DU

When city-slicker visitors step off the train at Llandudno Junction they're always surprised to discover such an extensive range of speciality grade caffeine mere steps from the North Wales station.

In many urban cafes you'd be lucky to find more than one option on espresso, but this village coffee shop boasts three – plus another on the brew bar. The hefty drinks menu is thanks to founder Jon Hughes who was a pioneer of the local coffee scene and the first to serve speciality in this neck of the woods. He slung 'spros from a Citroen HY van before crowdsourcing to launch his first bricks-and-mortar cafe.

INSIDER'S TIP POP IN BEFORE 9.30AM TO BAG A TAKEAWAY COFFEE FOR £2

Today Jon works with local roastery Heartland, selecting coffees to *'enthuse and excite guests'*. The roastery's Landmark blend makes a killer house espresso and Jon also chooses the monthly roster of single origins: *'We love a juicy natural and a wicked bourbon,'* he says.

A simple menu of toast, granola and cakes forms a fine pairing to the carefully crafted coffee, while the BYO lunch policy adds to the relaxed community vibe.

ESTABLISHED
2014

KEY ROASTER
Heartland
Coffee Roasters

BREWING METHOD
Espresso,
AeroPress,
Clever Dripper

MACHINE
Sanremo Zoe

GRINDER
Mythos One
Clima Pro,
Mahlkonig EK43

OPENING HOURS
Mon-Sat 8am-5pm
Sun 10am-4pm

---

www.providero.co.uk T: 01492 338220
f @providero 🐦 @providero 📷 @providero.junction

MAP №42 KING STREET COFFEE COMPANY

1 Lord Street Arcade, Wrexham Bus Station, Wrexham, Wales, LL11 1LF

From its spot within Wrexham Bus Station, King Street Coffee lifts commuters' spirits with velvety flat whites and friendly chat. In addition to the intricate latte art and expertly extracted espresso, a counter crammed with bejewelled cakes also helps make the work journey a little sweeter.

Owner Phil Gallanders is dedicated to creating a warm, friendly and high-quality experience at his flagship coffee shop. As a result of this careful attention to detail King Street scooped Best Coffee Shop in the 2018 Wrexham Tourism Awards.

INSIDER'S tip MISSED BREAKFAST? PAIR YOUR FLAT WHITE WITH A BUTTERY CRUMPET

Speciality grade beans hop across the border from Neighbourhood in Liverpool and form the basis of an espresso-led bill of drinks. Got time to kill before you catch the bus? Find a quiet nook and get stuck in to a quality latte and a wedge of Wagon Wheel traybake as you watch the world hurry by.

ESTABLISHED
2016

KEY ROASTER
Neighbourhood Coffee

BREWING METHOD
Espresso

MACHINE
Sanremo Verona TCS

GRINDER
Macap MXD

OPENING HOURS
Mon-Fri 7.30am-4.30pm
Sat 8.30am-4pm

BEANS AVAILABLE INSTORE

WIFI

DISABLED ACCESS

BRING YOUR OWN cup

---

www.kingstreetcoffee.co.uk

f @kingstreetcoffeecompany 🐦 @kingstcoffee 📷 @kingstcoffeecompany

MAP № 43 BANK STREET SOCIAL

5a Bank Street, Wrexham, Wales, LL11 1AH

Speciality coffee and craft beer collide at this sociable spot in the heart of Wrexham town centre.

Sister cafe to the popular King Street Coffee, Bank Street extends the brand's community-focused ethos and welcomes everyone for good chat and cracking caffeine. Its lively line-up of events also means there's usually something exciting going on, from art exhibitions and stand-up comedy sessions to spoken word and vinyl nights where you can bring along your records.

INSIDE'S TIP TREAT SOMEONE SPESH TO A HANDMADE BOX OF CRAFT BEERS

Whether you're making a morning visit or dropping by for an afternoon pick-me-up, you'll find a solid selection of quality drinks to choose from. Coffee is roasted by the gang at Neighbourhood Coffee in Liverpool, while craft beers are sourced from local breweries and artisan producers across the country. Ask founder Andy for his pick of the breweries — he knows his stuff.

In his ongoing efforts to make the coffee shop as sustainable as possible, earlier this year Andy made the switch from plastic to glass milk bottles from a local dairy.

ESTABLISHED
2017

KEY ROASTER
Neighbourhood
Coffee

BREWING METHOD
Espresso, filter

MACHINE
La Marzocco
Linea PB

GRINDER
Victoria Arduino
Mythos One

OPENING HOURS
Mon-Fri 9am-4pm
Sat 10am-4pm

BEANS AVAILABLE INSTORE

WIFI

DISABLED ACCESS

BRING YOUR OWN Cup

DOG FRIENDLY

f @BankStreetSocialWxm 🐦 @bankstsocial 📷 @bankstsocial

MAP N° 44 RIVERBANC

Bridge Street, Llangollen, Denbighshire, Wales, LL20 8PF

Most big-city hotels haven't cracked good coffee, so to discover speciality grade beans at your digs in rural North Wales is really rather special.

The former bank in the centre of Llangollen was refurbished at the end of 2018 to house SAS Outdoors' new HQ. And, with a cavernous space to fill, founder and adrenaline junkie Craig Forde included a ground floor coffee shop and collection of contemporary guest rooms in his grand plan.

INSIDER'S TIP SAMPLE THE LATEST SEASONAL GUEST FROM HASBEAN ON CHEMEX

Ringside views over the River Dee from the decking area and a consistent supply of quality espresso have made Riverbanc's cafe as popular with the locals as it is with its overnight guests. The coffee in question travels the short distance from Hasbean's Staffordshire roastery so every cup is stonkingly fresh.

Brunch is also big business here and the house specials include sweet and savoury waffles (try the grilled halloumi with rocket and spicy chilli jam). If you're swinging by later in the day, check out the line-up of wines, beers and pale ales.

ESTABLISHED
2018

KEY ROASTER
Hasbean

BREWING METHOD
Espresso,
Chemex, filter

MACHINE
Nuova Simonelli
Aurelia T3

GRINDER
Mythos One

OPENING HOURS
Mon-Thu 8am-4pm
Fri-Sat 8am-8.30pm
Sun 8am-4.30pm

Gluten FREE

BEANS AVAILABLE INSTORE

WIFI

CYCLE FRIENDLY

OUTDOOR Seating

DISABLED ACCESS

BRING YOUR OWN Cup

DOG FRIENDLY

www.riverbanc.co.uk   T: 01978 799903

f @riverbanc   🐦 @riverbanc   📷 @riverbanccafe

ᴺᵒ45 DYFI ROASTERY

29 Heol Maengwyn, Machynlleth, Powys, Wales, SY20 8EB

It's quite a USP being located within one of only six UNESCO biospheres in the UK. But even without the jaw-dropping scenery of the Dyfi Valley and the eclectic history of Machynlleth, you'd still be drawn in by the curious appeal of Dyfi Roastery.

This is a coffee shop, yes, but it's also a lifestyle store with a philosophy that's admirable and infectious. Provenance is king, and everything – from the furniture to the cups – is carefully selected. You can even buy the fixtures and fittings as the shop takes on an ever-changing form.

INSIDER'S TIP: FORGOTTEN YOUR REUSABLE CUP? BORROW ONE FROM THE TAKEAWAY LIBRARY

Guests (including Origin, Square Mile and Method) ably support Dyfi's home-roasted beans. And however you like your coffee brewed, the crew cover all bases with an armoury of kit which includes AeroPress, french press and cold brew. Fancy an artisan hot chocolate or cooling frappe? That's no problem, either.

After a browse through the selection of local pottery, home interiors and fashion finds, dive in to delicious cakes and cream teas baked in the roastery kitchen.

ESTABLISHED
2018

KEY ROASTER
Dyfi Roastery

BREWING METHOD
Espresso, AeroPress, V60, batch filter, french press

MACHINE
La Marzocco Linea PB ABR

GRINDER
Mythos One, Mahlkonig EK43T, Wilfa Svart, hand grinder

OPENING HOURS
Wed-Sat **9**am-**5**pm
Sun **10**am-**4**pm

BEANS AVAILABLE INSTORE

WIFI

CYCLE FRIENDLY

OUTDOOR SEATING

BRING YOUR OWN CUP

COFFEE COURSES

DOG FRIENDLY

www.dyfiroastery.com   T: 01654 703947

f @dyfiroasters   🐦 @dyfiroastery   📷 @dyfiroastery

ROASTERS

Unit 6, Cwrt Roger Mostyn, Builder Street, Llandudno, North Wales, LL30 1DS

If their enthusiastic energy is anything to go by, it's likely that the Heartland crew have actual espresso running through their veins.

The team's latest project has been to throw open the roastery doors and launch their own coffee bar (complete with Sanremo Opera 2.0). Caffeine lovers are invited to visit to sip their way through a selection of brews, then take home a bag of whatever they enjoyed most.

A new collab with local brewery Wild Horse means visitors can also sample the house coffee stout at the shipping container venue. Mr Mills' Circus (named after the second world war MI5 operation in which German double agents were hidden in Llandudno) features Heartland's Noe Rivera Colombian micro-lot.

THE TEAM'S LATEST PROJECT HAS BEEN TO THROW OPEN THE ROASTERY DOORS AND LAUNCH THEIR OWN COFFEE BAR

Away from the roastery, the team have set their sights on winning more converts beyond North Wales and are working hard to inspire cafes and restaurants with their range of directly traded micro-lots.

ESTABLISHED
2012

ROASTER
MAKE & SIZE

Coffee-Tech Ghibli 45kg

Coffee-Tech Ghibli 15kg

Coffee-Tech Solar 2kg

www.heartlandcoffi.co.uk   01492 878757

@heartlandcoffeeuk   @heartlandcoffi   @heartland.coffee

Nº 41
Providero –
Llandudno Junction

47 POBLADO COFFI

Unit 1, Y Barics, Nantlle, Caernarfon, Gwynedd, LL54 6BD

There are worse views to ponder while you work than the vista of Snowdon from Poblado Coffi's ex-quarrymen's-barracks roastery.

At this blustery valley setting some of the best beans in the world are respectfully – and sometimes experimentally – roasted to create a range of exceptional single origins and blends.

Currently a 15kg Giesen does the job but it wasn't long ago that Poblado was a garden-shed operation. From those humble beginnings the business has grown to become a beacon of the burgeoning Welsh speciality scene.

'AT THIS BLUSTERY VALLEY SETTING SOME OF THE BEST BEANS IN THE WORLD ARE ROASTED'

In addition to his aim to treat customers to stonking beans, founder Steffan Huws also has ethical considerations at heart and ensures that the top-notch lots he buys from Africa, the Americas and Asia are scrupulously fairly traded. Long-term relationships with growers are prioritised and certifications – including Rainforest Alliance – wholly supported, so that the coffee is sustainable to the last drop.

ESTABLISHED
2013

ROASTER
MAKE & SIZE
Giesen 15kg

OPEN
TO THE PUBLIC

COFFEE
COURSES

BEANS
AVAILABLE

www.pobladocoffi.co.uk | 01286 882555

f @pobladocoffi @pobladocoffi @poblado_coffi

GREATER MANCHESTER & CHESHIRE

Fig + Sparrow   № 60

Locations are approximate

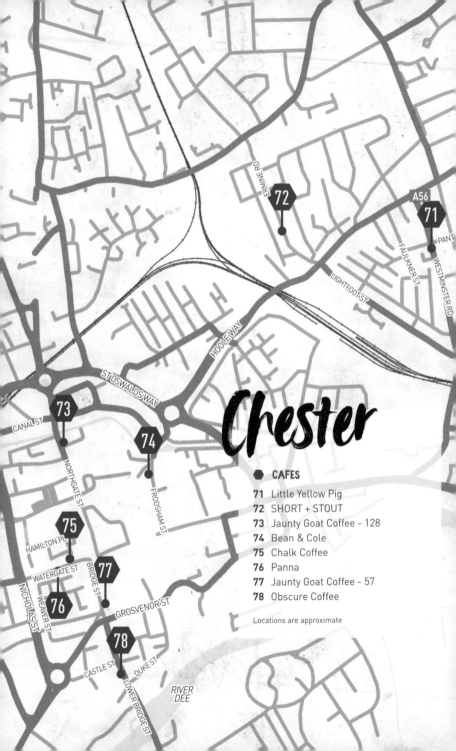

Chester

● **CAFES**

71 Little Yellow Pig
72 SHORT + STOUT
73 Jaunty Goat Coffee - 128
74 Bean & Cole
75 Chalk Coffee
76 Panna
77 Jaunty Goat Coffee - 57
78 Obscure Coffee

Locations are approximate

NORTHERN QUARTER

ANCOATS

⬡ CAFES

51 Heart and Graft Coffee Shop
52 Grindsmith Coffee Pod
53 Pot Kettle Black – Barton Arcade
54 Grindsmith – Bridge Street
55 Federal Cafe & Bar – Deansgate
56 Hampton & Voûis
57 Federal Cafe & Bar – Nicholas Croft
58 Atkinsons The Mackie Mayor
59 Just Between Friends
60 Fig + Sparrow
61 Foundation Coffee House – NQ
62 Takk Coffee House – Tariff Street
63 Ancoats Coffee Co.
64 Foundation Coffee House – Whitworth
65 Takk Espresso Bar
66 Takk – University Green

⬡ TRAINING

80 Extract Coffee Roasters

Locations are approximate

Manchester

№48 GRIND & TAMP

45 Bridge Street, Ramsbottom, Bury, Greater Manchester, BL0 9AD

Weekly switched-up house roasts and a plethora of guests and brewing equipment are not just the preserve of Manchester's Northern Quarter – as Ramsbottom's residents know.

Their local coffee shop boasts four grinders which feature beans from the likes of Berlin's The Barn, London's Square Mile and Liverpool's Neighbourhood, alongside house roasts from Atkinsons, North Star and Common Ground.

INSIDER'S TIP DM THE TEAM ON FRIDAYS TO BAG A LOAF OF FRESHLY BAKED SOURDOUGH THE NEXT DAY

Visitors can polish their tasting skills at one of the regular coffee cupping sessions or speciality chocolate tastings with Manchester's Dormouse Chocolates.

Fuel the fun via the chalkboard of brunch and lunch specials and feed your comfort-food cravings with stalwarts such as pimped grilled cheese, and sausage and egg muffins.

ESTABLISHED
2013

KEY ROASTER
Multiple roasters

BREWING METHOD
Espresso, V60, Chemex, AeroPress, cold brew

MACHINE
Sanremo Verona RS

GRINDER
Mahlkonig K30 x 2, Victoria Arduino Mythos One, DIP DK-30

OPENING HOURS
Mon **8.30**am-**3**pm
Thu-Sat **8.30**am-**3**pm
Sun **10**am-**3.30**pm

www.grindandtampcoffee.uk   T: 01706 558030

f @grindandtampcoffee   🐦 @grind_tamp   📷 @grind_tamp

MAP № 49 THE SNUG COFFEE HOUSE

67a Market Street, Atherton, Greater Manchester, M46 0DA

Duck through an arch off Atherton's Market Street, leave the bustle behind and settle in at the aptly named Snug Coffee House.

The relaxed open-plan space has all the comforts of an eclectically decorated home, but with the benefits of speciality coffee and a fully licenced bar. Locals gather at the grassroots music venue to catch up with friends, discover new music or just kick back – usually with a coffee in close proximity.

INSIDER'S TIP DIARIES AT THE READY: SNUG HOSTS REGULAR LIVE MUSIC AND COMEDY EVENTS

Filter options are attentively brewed from beans that have made the short hop from Joe Black in Liverpool, but keep your eyes peeled for additional guest coffees.

Community plays an important role at Snug and the team choose to support local producers when sourcing everything from cakes (there's always a gluten-free option) to wildflower honey.

Crafty types are also welcome and can often be found knitting or getting stuck in to a bit of crochet while sipping their choice from the wide range of loose-leaf teas.

ESTABLISHED
2015

KEY ROASTER
Joe Black Coffee

BREWING METHOD
Espresso, filter, Chemex, cafetiere

MACHINE
Iberital

GRINDER
Iberital

OPENING HOURS
Mon-Sat 8am-4pm
Sun 10am-4pm

 Gluten FREE

 WIFI

 CYCLE FRIENDLY

 OUTDOOR seating

 DISABLED ACCESS

 BRING YOUR OWN cup

 DOG FRIENDLY

www.thesnugatherton.com   T: 01942 875430

f @thesnugatherton   🐦 @snugatherton   📷 @thesnugatherton

№50 GRINDSMITH – MEDIA CITY

Unit 5-6, The Garage, MediaCityUK, Salford, Greater Manchester, M50 2BS

Positioned at the heart of Media City, Grindsmith's Salford venue is a speciality sanctuary for the local workforce of broadcasters, journalists and business folk.

The contemporary cafe has been designed with its customers in mind and plentiful plug sockets, huge floor-to-ceiling windows and a consistent supply of incredible caffeine make it a find if you're looking to knuckle down to some hard graft or hold an informal meeting. Others visit simply to soak up the atmosphere and unwind while watching baristas artfully craft AeroPress and pourovers from beans roasted across the city.

INSIDER'S TIP LOOK OUT FOR THE FOURTH GRINDSMITH VENUE – COMING TO MANCHESTER AIRPORT IN 2020

It's not just the coffee that stops heads slumping on keyboards; pre-work and lunchtime visitors fuel up with protein-packed power bowls, eggs benedict and stacks of buttermilk pancakes.

There's also a weekend brunch menu for those taking a stroll along the nearby canal.

ESTABLISHED
2015

KEY ROASTER
Grindsmith
Coffee Roasters

BREWING METHOD
Espresso, Kalita
Wave, AeroPress

MACHINE
Victoria Arduino
Black Eagle
Gravitech

GRINDER
Mythos One x 2,
Mahlkonig EK43

OPENING HOURS
Mon-Fri 7.30am-6pm
Sat 9am-6pm
Sun 9am-5pm

Gluten FREE

BEANS AVAILABLE / INSTORE

WIFI

CYCLE FRIENDLY

DOG FRIENDLY

---

www.grindsmith.com   T: 07495 850032

f @grindsmith   🐦 @grindsmiths   📷 @grindsmithcoffee

MAP No. 51 HEART AND GRAFT COFFEE SHOP

70 Yorkshire Street, Salford, M3 5EG

Purple may once have been a colour reserved for royalty, but it's safe to say that this stalwart of the northern coffee scene has earned the right to sport its aubergine-hued brand colour.

Heart and Graft has roasted in the city since 2012, keeping venues across the North stocked with its high-grade beans. Yet this is its first cafe and, for fans who've fallen for H&G coffee elsewhere, it offers an excellent opportunity for immersion in the spectrum of Heart and Graft blends, single origins and micro-lots.

INSIDER'S TIP BREAD HEAD? FILL YOUR BOOTS WITH UNLIMITED SOURDOUGH FOR £3.50

It's not only coffee buffs who stop by; this is a sanctuary for anyone looking to escape the madness of Manchester city centre. Interiors blooming with floral illustrations and a collection of tropical houseplants create a chilled-out botanical vibe.

Community events extend the invite to all via regular yoga classes, discussion evenings and live music gigs, while aspiring baristas can book on to one of the brewing masterclasses.

ESTABLISHED
2018

KEY ROASTER
Heart and Graft

BREWING METHOD
Espresso,
batch brew

MACHINE
La Marzocco
Strada ABR

GRINDER
Compak F10,
Mahlkonig EK43

OPENING HOURS
Mon-Fri
7.30am-3.30pm

www.heartandgraft.co.uk   T: 07743 895763

🐦 @heartandgraft   📷 @heartandgraft

№ 52 GRINDSMITH COFFEE POD

Greengate Square, Victoria Bridge Street, Manchester, M3 5AS

For those seeking head space – and quality caffeine – in Manchester's bustling business district, Grindsmith's Greengate Square venue offers a serene coffee break.

The timber-clad Coffee Pod's location, ringside fountain seats and zen vibe make it all too easy for a lunch hour to slip away in the flash of a filter. Grab a spot on one of the repurposed-pallet benches and look over the water as you tuck in to a hunk of homemade cake.

INSIDER'S tip TRY THE GRINDSMITH COLD BREW CONCENTRATE – IT MAKES A KILLER CAFFEINATED GIN COOLER

The expert baristas have tuned in to the leisurely pace and like to take their time over the beans (roasted across the city at HQ). Consequently, there's a huge range of pourover options alongside the espresso crafted on the La Marzocco machine.

As the original Grindsmith cafe, this is where the micro-chain's reputation for epic coffee started and its rep remains untarnished, thanks to impeccably presented espresso based drinks.

ESTABLISHED
2014

KEY ROASTER
Grindsmith
Coffee Roasters

BREWING METHOD
Espresso,
pourover

MACHINE
La Marzocco
GS3

GRINDER
Mythos One,
Mazzer Royal

OPENING HOURS
Mon-Fri 8am-5pm
Sat 9am-5pm
Sun 10am-5pm

BEANS AVAILABLE INSTORE

WIFI

CYCLE FRIENDLY

OUTDOOR SEATING

DISABLED ACCESS

DOG FRIENDLY

---

www.grindsmith.com T: 07496 798220
f @grindsmith 🐦 @grindsmiths 📷 @grindsmithcoffee

MAP№ 53 POT KETTLE BLACK – BARTON ARCADE

Barton Arcade, Deansgate, Manchester, M3 2BW

The trend that's seen speciality cafes match their superior coffee offering with equally impressive food continues to gather momentum, yet this Barton Arcade fave has specialised in indulgent NZ-inspired brunching since it opened over half a decade ago.

As a result, the casual dining spot has garnered a wide spectrum of loyal patrons: coffee folk perch near the tiled bar to watch baristas craft espresso from Workshop beans; millennials gather at the communal tables to pap pics of their black forest french toast; and workers sit in the arcade and catch up on emails over batch brew and fresh pain aux raisins.

INSIDER'S TIP BOOK THE NEW PRIVATE DINING SPACE FOR A SPECIAL-OCCASION BRUNCH

Everything is crafted from scratch in the bakery and kitchen, and the team's efforts to create a unique casual-dining experience has scored PKB a number of regional awards, including Manchester Food and Drink's Best Cafe. Pay a visit and toast the coffee shop's success with a cocktail from the boozy drinks bill.

ESTABLISHED
2014

KEY ROASTER
Workshop Coffee

BREWING METHOD
Espresso, V60, AeroPress, batch brew

MACHINE
La Marzocco Linea PB

GRINDER
Mahlkonig EK43, Mythos One

OPENING HOURS
Mon-Sat 8am-7pm
Sun 9am-5pm

Gluten FREE

BEANS AVAILABLE / INSTORE

WIFI

CYCLE FRIENDLY

OUTDOOR seating

DISABLED ACCESS

BRING YOUR OWN Cup.

DOG FRIENDLY

www.potkettleblackltd.co.uk
f @pkbcoffee 🐦 @pkbcoffee 📷 @pkbcoffee

MAP № 54 GRINDSMITH – BRIDGE STREET

62 Bridge Street, Manchester, M3 3BW

Deansgate's workforce was gutted when Grindsmith's stalwart cafe closed at the start of 2019. Happily, broken hearts were quickly mended when a new outpost opened close by.

The Bridge Street branch is hard to miss: just look for the colourful floral mosaic which blooms on its tall facade. Inside, Grindsmith's trademark industrial decor meets marbled walls, blush-pink features, houseplants and neon lights, setting the mood for speciality-standard caffeine and serious brunching.

INSIDE'S tip ORDER BEANS, EQUIPMENT AND GIFT VOUCHERS ON THE GRINDSMITH WEBSITE

Coffee is cooked up across the city at the new roastery in Ancoats. Pair a fresh-from-the-drum batch brew with a late breakfast of homemade beetroot hummus and avocado on sourdough. If you're in a rush, download the Grindsmith app and order your take-out en route.

Aspiring espresso slingers can take a seat on the ground floor and watch the pro baristas pull shots from the slick VA Black Eagle. Brought the whole gang? Follow the neon 'this way' sign to the backroom for a more spacious set-up overlooking the open kitchen.

ESTABLISHED
2019

KEY ROASTER
Grindsmith
Coffee Roaster

BREWING METHOD
Espresso,
Seraphim
Brewer

MACHINE
Victoria Arduino
Black Eagle
Gravitech

GRINDER
Mythos One x 2,
Mahlkonig EK43
Mini

OPENING HOURS
Mon-Fri 7.30am-6.30pm
Sat 9am-6pm
Sun 10am-5pm

Gluten FREE

BEANS AVAILABLE INSTORE

WIFI

DISABLED ACCESS

DOG FRIENDLY

---

www.grindsmith.com T: 07496 798220

f @grindsmith 🐦 @grindsmiths 📷 @grindsmithcoffee

MAP № 55 FEDERAL CAFE & BAR - DEANSGATE

194 Deansgate, Manchester, M3 3ND

Sister to the Nicholas Croft original, Federal's new venue is set in an impressive palazzo-style building and gleams with the newness of its 2019 debut.

The team have skilfully pulled off the tricky task of transplanting the easygoing Aussie vibe that makes the flagship gaff so welcoming: squishy mustard-coloured sofas, reclaimed wooden floors and leafy plants all contribute to the home-from-home feel.

INSIDER'S TIP: THE PASTEL DE NATA ARE A SPECIALITY – GRAB ONE TO-GO WITH YOUR FLAT WHITE

Everything kicks off at 7am with flatties and short blacks fuelling the city's workforce for the day. Speciality blasphemers, meanwhile, start their morning with a dirty chai latte spiked with a shot of espresso. Batch brew and AeroPress are also on hand and all of the drinks are meticulously made with beans from Ozone.

Brunch service kicks off as soon as the doors open and those in the know choose cheddar corn fritters stacked with bacon or smoked salmon, avocado and poached eggs. Pair it with a cold brew over ice or choose an Espresso Martini from the 'Something Stronger' list if it's the weekend.

ESTABLISHED
2019

KEY ROASTER
Ozone Coffee Roasters

BREWING METHOD
Espresso, AeroPress, cold brew, batch brew

MACHINE
La Marzocco Linea PB

GRINDER
Mahlkonig EK43, Victoria Arduino Mythos One

OPENING HOURS
Mon-Fri 7am-6pm
Sat 8am-6pm
Sun 8am-5pm

 Gluten FREE

 BEANS AVAILABLE / INSTORE

 WIFI

 CYCLE FRIENDLY

 DISABLED ACCESS

 BRING YOUR OWN CUP

 COFFEE COURSES

DOG FRIENDLY

---

www.federalcafe.co.uk T: 01618 330890

f @federalcafebar 🐦 @federalcafebar 📷 @federalcafebar

MAP №56 HAMPTON & VOÚIS

31 Princess Street, Manchester, M2 4EW

Buckets of natural light, perfectly poured latte art and neatly compiled bowls of colourful ingredients guarantee that your #brunch snaps at this Manchester cafe will earn a lot of love on social.

The glamorous set-up is a photographer's dream: white walls are adorned with geometric fittings, flowers and plants; a polished-concrete bar hosts a sleek Sanremo Café Racer machine; and plush velvet chairs line a dark-wood window table overlooking Manchester Town Hall.

Keen to ensure that the quality of the food and coffee matches the high-end interiors, founders Nicky Hampton and Niko Voúis have enlisted the help of some of the North's finest producers. Alongside Buxton Roastery beans you'll find organic sourdough and pastries from Trove Bakery, eco-friendly Aura Chai and brownies by Brown & Blond.

INSIDER'S TIP A HOT/ICED DRINKS MENU OFFERS TURMERIC LATTE, ROSE MATCHA AND VEGAN AFFOGATO

Not that you'll want to fill up on anything too carby before ordering brunch. The menu offers a nourishing twist on British and Mediterranean classics with dishes such as toasted sourdough with black olive tapenade, burrata, cherry tomatoes and basil dressing.

ESTABLISHED
2018

KEY ROASTER
Buxton Roastery

BREWING METHOD
Espresso, V60, AeroPress

MACHINE
Sanremo Café Racer

GRINDER
Sanremo SR83E

OPENING HOURS
Mon-Fri 7am-6pm
Sat 9am-6pm
Sun 10am-5pm

BEANS AVAILABLE INSTORE

WIFI

DOG FRIENDLY

www.hamptonandvouis.co.uk

f @hamptonandvouis 🐦 @hamptonandvouis 📷 @hamptonandvouis

MAP 57 FEDERAL CAFE & BAR – NICHOLAS CROFT

9 Nicholas Croft, Manchester, M4 1EY

The antipodean spirit is strong at this city centre cafe and bar, thanks to its buzzy collision of friendly metropolitan vibes, treat-yo-self food and killer brews.

Coffee is taken extremely seriously but the team don't let that get in the way of the good times, even in the pursuit of getting each cup just-so.

Ozone supplies the beans, while a dedicated team of expert baristas conjure up the rest of the magic. Choose from espresso, V60 and AeroPress preps and don't overlook the cold brew – the climate here might not be Aussie but the attitude certainly is.

INSIDER'S TIP GO VIRTUOUS WITH A SUPERMAN – A JUICY MIX OF BANANA, APPLE, KALE AND AVOCADO

Brunch at Federal is a thing of great (and generous) beauty and provides the axis around which the cafe's warm-hearted culture spins. French toast with macerated berries, white chocolate and almond crumble, whipped vanilla mascarpone and salted caramel calls for a flat white chaser.

And if you're settling down to make an afternoon of it, turn to the brunch cocktail menu. Two for a tenner after 3pm? Sold.

ESTABLISHED
2014

KEY ROASTER
Ozone Coffee Roasters

BREWING METHOD
Espresso, V60, AeroPress, cold brew

MACHINE
La Marzocco Linea PB

GRINDER
Mahlkonig EK43, Victoria Arduino Mythos One

OPENING HOURS
Mon-Fri 7.30am-6pm
Sat 8am-6pm
Sun 8am-5pm

---

www.federalcafe.co.uk   T: 01614 250974

f @federalcafebar   🐦 @federalcafebar   📷 @federalcafebar

BE CONTEMPORARY.
STAY TRADITIONAL.

We understand that speed of service is vital. That's why we created our unique & multi award winning chai infusion. Perfectly blended by a barista for a barista.

CAFFEINE FREE

VEGAN FRIENDLY

ALLERGEN FREE

100% NATURAL

Say hello, we can chat all day!
hello@hennyandjoes.co.uk | @hennyandjoes | hennyandjoes.co.uk

MAP №58 ATKINSONS THE MACKIE MAYOR

1 Eagle Street, Manchester, M4 5BU

Hipster food halls are popping up across the country and, sure, plenty have a speciality coffee shop among the tribe of indies, but how many of them are roasting beans on-site?

When Atkinsons moved in to the corner spot that wraps around Manchester's Mackie Mayor in 2017, founder Ian Steel installed a 100-year-old Uno (the world's first vintage roaster restored with 3D-engineered parts) so that visitors could watch the beans being roasted and delve into the story behind the coffee while they sipped cappuccinos and cortados.

INSIDER'S tip TRY OUT THE NEW SINGLE ORIGINS AT FREE WEEKLY CUPPING SESSIONS

Espresso, pourover and batch brew are complemented by an extensive range of cakes, pastries and savouries baked daily at Atkinsons' Lancaster HQ. The team specialise in gluten-free and vegan bakes, so there's something for everyone to sink their teeth into.

Late opening hours put Atkinsons' expertly roasted beans to good use after hours in an inventive bill of cocktails. Go trad with an Espresso Martini or Irish coffee – or, if you're feeling just a little bit *Mad Men*, loosen your tie and order a Coffee Old Fashioned.

ESTABLISHED
2017

KEY ROASTER
Atkinsons
Coffee Roasters

BREWING METHOD
Espresso,
Marco SP9,
Kalita Wave

MACHINE
Sanremo Opera

GRINDER
Mythos One
Clima Pro,
Mahlkonig EK43

OPENING HOURS
Mon 8am-2pm
Tue-Thu 8am-10pm
Fri 8am-11pm
Sat 9am-11pm
Sun 9am-8pm

Gluten FREE | BEANS AVAILABLE INSTORE | WIFI | CYCLE FRIENDLY | OUTDOOR SEATING | DISABLED ACCESS | BRING YOUR OWN CUP | COFFEE COURSES | DOG FRIENDLY

---

www.thecoffeehopper.com T: 01524 65470

f @atkinsonscoffee 🐦 @coffeehopper 📷 @atkinsons.coffee

№59 JUST BETWEEN FRIENDS

56 Tib Street, Manchester, M4 1LG

Consistently great coffee and a slick setting make this pocket-sized cafe a popular spot with both locals and tipped-off weekenders.

A not-so-secret combination of quality single origin brews and tasty homemade food quickly put Just Between Friends on the Manchester coffee map when it opened in 2018. The cat is now truly out of the bag, so it's not unusual to find customers spilling from the bi-fold windows onto the cluster of chairs on Tib Street.

London's Assembly feeds the La Marzocco with a choice house espresso, while the filter spot is filled by regularly changing global guest roasts such as Cloud Picker (Dublin), Morgon (Gothenburg) and Panther (Miami).

INSIDER'S TIP SUMMERTIME? SWAP YOUR USUAL ORDER FOR AN ICED VERSION

Insta-worthy interiors and a friendly vibe make it all too easy to lose an hour here although the expertly crafted coffee is worth taking your time over. Nab a leather stool in the window, order a chilli-spiked avocado toast and then chase your second espresso with a sizeable chunk of blondie.

ESTABLISHED
2018

KEY ROASTER
Assembly Coffee

BREWING METHOD
Espresso, V60, batch brew

MACHINE
La Marzocco Linea PB

GRINDER
Victoria Arduino Mythos One

OPENING HOURS
Mon-Fri 7.30am-4pm
Sat-Sun 8.30am-4pm

www.justbetweenfriendscoffee.com

f @Justbetweenfriends   🐦 @justbetweenfri2   📷 @justbetweenfriendscoffee

MAP№60 FIG + SPARROW

20 Oldham Street, Northern Quarter, Manchester, M1 1JN

This Northern Quarter favourite has had a reshuffle this year, moving the espresso machine to the front of the cafe for a smoother take-out operation and adding extra tables and chairs so that even more speciality fans can lounge while revelling in their carefully prepared coffee.

London's Climpson & Sons continues to provide its Estate Blend for the house espresso, while Wiltshire's Girls Who Grind has taken up a new residency as the guest single origin. As a female-led business (Jan and Emily Dixon launched Fig + Sparrow seven years ago), working with the all-female roastery was a no-brainer.

INSIDER'S TIP THE WINDOW BENCH IS PERFECT FOR MAGAZINE SKIMMING AND PEOPLE WATCHING

The top-notch coffee is complemented by a wholesome and hearty menu of homemade food, as well as a killer soundtrack of handpicked tunes. Crack on with some work or catch up with friends over a steaming bowl of chunky soup or a generous slice of blackberry, rose, lemon and pistachio cake.

Then, well-fed and caffeinated, take the opportunity to browse the curated collection of designware in-store.

ESTABLISHED
2013

KEY ROASTER
Climpson
& Sons

BREWING METHOD
Espresso,
AeroPress, V60,
Chemex

MACHINE
La Marzocco
Linea PB

GRINDER
Victoria Arduino
Mythos One,
Mahlkonig EK43

OPENING HOURS
Mon-Fri 8am-7pm
Sat-Sun 9am-7pm

www.figandsparrow.co.uk   T: 07815 137563
f @figsparrow   🐦 @figsparrow   📷 @figsparrow

MAP Nº 61 FOUNDATION COFFEE HOUSE – NQ

Sevendale House, Lever Street, Manchester, M1 1JB

Manchester's Northern Quarter hums with creativity, a vibe perfectly captured at spacious and design-led Foundation Coffee House. Inspiration and relaxation are to be sourced in equal measure here, alongside the finest food and artisan coffee.

Whether you're dashing in for your morning kick-starter or settling down to a day of laptop tickling, the welcome is warm and inviting. A regular events programme, which includes yoga sessions and movie nights, provides yet further reason to drop by.

Origin beans form the basis of all of the brews, from the espresso based classics pulled through the La Marzocco to the V60, Chemex and AeroPress filters. The Foundation team are keen experimenters and regularly test new additional brewing methods.

INSIDER'S TIP TAKE PART IN REGULAR OPEN MIC NIGHTS, DJ SESSIONS AND STREET FOOD POP-UPS

A carefully crafted blend of cloves and cinnamon in the homemade chai provides a comforting alternative to coffee, while an enticing menu of breakfast and brunch dishes further fuels creative endeavours.

ESTABLISHED
2015

KEY ROASTER
Origin Coffee Roasters

BREWING METHOD
Espresso, Kalita Wave, V60, AeroPress, Chemex

MACHINE
La Marzocco Linea PB

GRINDER
Mythos One

OPENING HOURS
Mon 7am-6pm
Tue-Thu 7am-8pm
Fri 7am-10pm
Sat 9am-10pm
Sun 9am-8pm

Gluten FREE

BEANS AVAILABLE INSTORE

WIFI

CYCLE FRIENDLY

OUTDOOR seating

DISABLED ACCESS

BRING YOUR OWN Cup

COFFEE COURSES

DOG FRIENDLY

www.foundationcoffeehouse.co.uk   T: 01612 388633

f @fdncoffee   @fdncoffee

MAP № 62 TAKK COFFEE HOUSE – TARIFF STREET

6 Tariff Street, Northern Quarter, Manchester, M1 2FF

The original in Takk's trio of Manchester cafes, this Northern Quarter stalwart has blazed a speciality trail in the city since 2013.

Set in a charming red brick building which speaks of the area's mercantile past, it's a firm favourite among those seeking consistently fine coffee and food.

The house espresso – unique to Takk – showcases beans from Finca Miravalle in El Salvador and is expertly roasted in Bristol by Clifton Coffee. Every week visitors are tempted by four new single origin guest roasts. Chose from a multitude of filter options, or drink as espresso paired with Stephenson's Lancashire milk.

INSIDER'S TIP DON'T FORGET TO PICK UP A LOAF OF SOURDOUGH, BAKED LOCALLY AT POLLEN

While the Takk crew are pretty serious about coffee, they also love to create seriously tasty grub. As a result the menu combines wholesomeness with indulgence (smoked streaky, smashed avo and chipotle ketchup on sourdough being a delicious example). If you're also in the mood for something sweet, chase your choice with a slice of sticky homemade cake.

ESTABLISHED
2013

KEY ROASTER
Clifton Coffee Roasters

BREWING METHOD
Espresso, V60, Chemex, AeroPress, batch brew

MACHINE
La Marzocco Linea PB Auto Brew Ratio

GRINDER
Mahlkonig EK43, Mythos One Clima Pro

OPENING HOURS
Mon-Fri 8am-5pm
Sat 9am-5pm
Sun 10am-5pm

Gluten FREE

BEANS AVAILABLE INSTORE

WIFI

CYCLE FRIENDLY

OUTDOOR seating

BRING YOUR OWN cup

COFFEE COURSES

DOG FRIENDLY

www.takkmcr.com
f @takkmcr 🐦 @takkmcr 📷 @takkmcr

MAP No. 63 ANCOATS COFFEE CO.

Unit 9 Royal Mills, 17 Redhill Street, Manchester, M4 5BA

A nyone with a penchant for history would be chuffed to sip a coffee in this repurposed cotton mill which was once at the heart of the industrial revolution.

The iconic red brick walls and stunning sculptured glass ceiling of Ancoats' roastery cafe within Royal Mills make a phenomenal backdrop to the expert coffee craft going down. Beans for the VA Black Eagle machine and well-equipped brew bar are bronzed in the same room, and the team adopt a light roasting style which allows the full spectrum of flavours to shine.

Curious visitors who've stumbled across this hidden gem can watch the roasting process before sampling the exclusively single origin offering (with a chunk of the legendary banana loaf) in the cafe.

INSIDER'S TIP A GLASS ROOF MAKES 'ALFRESCO' SIPPING POSSIBLE, WHATEVER THE WEATHER

If the experience sparks your interest, regular home brewing workshops are available, while community events such as kitchen takeovers and barista showdowns also take place.

Can't make it to the roastery to sample the latest lot? Order beans online and fuel a coffee revolution in your own kitchen.

ESTABLISHED
2013

KEY ROASTER
Ancoats Coffee Co.

BREWING METHOD
Espresso,
AeroPress,
batch brew,
pourover,
Chemex,
cold brew

MACHINE
Victoria Arduino
VA388 Black
Eagle

GRINDER
Mythos One x 2,
Mahlkonig EK43,
Ditting ICR804

OPENING HOURS
Mon-Fri **8**am-**6**pm
Sat **9**am-**5**pm
Sun **10**am-**5**pm

Gluten FREE

BEANS AVAILABLE INSTORE

WIFI

CYCLE FRIENDLY

DISABLED ACCESS

BRING YOUR OWN Cup

DOG FRIENDLY

---

www.ancoats-coffee.co.uk   T: 01612 283211

f @ancoatscoffeeco   🐦 @ancoatscoffeeco   📷 @ancoatscoffeeco

MAP № 64 FOUNDATION COFFEE HOUSE – WHITWORTH

Whitworth Street, Manchester, M1 6JD

For a second helping of interior inspo and contemporary caffeine, head to Foundation's sister cafe at Whitworth Locke aparthotel.

In line with the original Northern Quarter venue, the comprehensive drinks menu covers the classics (espresso, ristretto, macchiato), flags up some out-there options (beetroot latte) and concludes with a few choices your barista may have to explain (kevlar, red eye, bulletproof).

INSIDER'S TIP REGULAR CLASSES TEACH PUNTERS HOW TO BREW COFFEE AT HOME AND PERFECT LATTE ART

Beans come exclusively from Origin and are transformed via the La Marzocco. Chemex and AeroPress are also on hand to enjoy in the industrial-urban atmosphere. Look out, too, for cold brew which has enjoyed a 24-hour steep to extract the full complexity of flavours.

The menu of all-day brunch dishes also takes a progressive approach and includes reinvented classics such as mushrooms on sourdough with red pepper ragu.

Whether swinging by to do a little work or meeting with friends, upgrade your coffee order with a breakfast of overnight oats with berries and pecans. Come evening, the signature Espresso Martini offers further thrills.

ESTABLISHED
2018

KEY ROASTER
Origin Coffee Roasters

BREWING METHOD
Espresso, V60, AeroPress, Kalita Wave

MACHINE
La Marzocco Linea PB ABR

GRINDER
Mythos One, Mahlkonig EK43

OPENING HOURS
Mon-Thu 7am-9pm
Fri-Sat 7am-10pm
Sun 7am-8pm

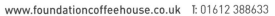

www.foundationcoffeehouse.co.uk   T: 01612 388633
f @fdncoffee   @ @fdncoffee

MAP №65 TAKK ESPRESSO BAR

Unit 1, Hatch, Oxford Road, Manchester, M1 7ED

The recipe for success at this espresso bar is certainly unorthodox: take a shipping container, slot it under a flyover, sprinkle it with Scandi influence and use it as a base for serving great coffee. However, unorthodox works and, as part of the uber-cool Hatch development, Takk shares in the kudos of awards won for innovative food retail.

The cafe scoops busy students and workers off the thrumming Oxford Road corridor and offers them an oasis of calm, filled with excellent brews and cakes. The big windows and pared-back decor invite you to kick back. Alternatively, head to the urban-chic roof terrace for a spot of people watching.

INSIDE'S TIP SISTER VENUE ÖL IS JUST NEXT DOOR AND ON HAND TO FULFIL YOUR CRAFT BEER AND NATURAL WINE NEEDS

The caffeine conscious from the surrounding university campus visit for Takk's North Projekt single origin as well as guest coffees from international roasters such as The Barn and Coffee Collective. And all of the beans are brought to life by a cheerily knowledgeable team at the La Marzocco Linea.

ESTABLISHED
2017

KEY ROASTER
Clifton Coffee
Roasters

BREWING METHOD
Espresso,
batch filter

MACHINE
La Marzocco
Linea PB Auto
Brew Ratio

GRINDER
Mythos One
Clima Pro,
Mahlkonig EK43

OPENING HOURS
Mon-Fri 8am-6pm
Sat 10am-6pm
Sun 10am-5pm

www.takkmcr.com
f @takkmcr 🐦 @takkmcr 📷 @takkmcr

MAP №66 TAKK – UNIVERSITY GREEN

138 Oxford Road, Manchester, M13 9GP

The third (and latest) addition to the Takk empire enjoys a middle-of-campus location where it fuels the frantic laptop tapping of a never-ending flow of students and academics.

Scrupulously selected single origins rule here and vacuum-freezing tech means the rare varieties and vintage micro-lot coffees always get top marks for freshness.

INSIDER'S TIP FOR A DEEP DIVE INTO THE WONDERS OF COFFEE, JOIN A 30-MINUTE GUIDED TASTING SESH

The house beans are crafted exclusively for Takk by Clifton Coffee Roasters, ably assisted by weekly changing international guests such as Koppi, Morgon and Holistik. Unsure what to go for? Make it easy by picking the W.B.D (what baristas drink) option.

The food's great too: carefully sourced ingredients are crafted with creative execution. Feed your brain with an order of brioche french toast or 'nduja, poached eggs and salsa verde.

ESTABLISHED
2019

KEY ROASTER
Clifton Coffee
Roasters

BREWING METHOD
Espresso,
batch filter,
Clever Dripper

MACHINE
La Marzocco
Strada AV ABR

GRINDER
Mythos One,
Mythos Two,
Mahlkonig
EK43 S

OPENING HOURS
Mon-Fri **7.30**am-**7**pm

 Gluten FREE

 BEANS AVAILABLE / INSTORE

 WIFI

 CYCLE FRIENDLY

 OUTDOOR SEATING

 DISABLED ACCESS

 BRING YOUR OWN CUP

 COFFEE COURSES

 DOG FRIENDLY

www.takkmcr.com

f @takkmcr　🐦 @takkmcr　📷 @takkmcr

HASBEAN

Flavours,
Relationships,
Quality

At HASBEAN, we believe investing in quality and relationships is the only sustainable way to produce coffee and run a business.

We focus on roasting a wide range of specialty coffee to order 5 days a week, reflecting the diversity of flavour that varietal, terroir, and farming skill can offer. By building long-term relationships with our producers, we enable them to experiment whilst having the certainty their coffees will reach customers who value them.

Life is too short for bad coffee.

hasbean.co.uk

MAP №67 NOOK

111 Heaton Moor Road, Heaton Moor, Stockport, Greater Manchester, SK4 4HY

Inspired to establish a community space where Heaton Moor locals could meet for coffee, craft beer and delicious grub, Jake McGrath took over Nook in 2019.

His vision was to create the kind of place where people would feel free to drop in at almost any time of day to catch up with friends – and make new ones.

Jake and team have pulled it off in style: arrive early to grab a ManCoCo flat white on the walk to work, carve out some mid-morning me-time with an Atkinsons V60 and the newspaper, meet chums for lunch, or drop in on one of the evening music sessions and fuel the fun with an Espresso Martini.

INSIDE'S TIP HEAVY NIGHT? ORDER THE MORNING AFTER JUICE BLEND OF APPLE, BEETROOT AND FENNEL

The eccentric decor (doors on the ceiling, poetry scribbled on the walls and Polaroid picture bunting) and lively line-up of events add to the make-yourself-at-home atmosphere.

Find a cosy corner, order something tasty from the menu and revel in the Nook experience.

ESTABLISHED
2019

KEY ROASTER
ManCoCo

BREWING METHOD
Espresso,
AeroPress,
Chemex, V60

MACHINE
La Marzocco
Linea PB

GRINDER
Sanremo

OPENING HOURS
Mon-Wed 8.30am-9pm
Thu-Fri 8.30am-11pm
Sat 9am-11pm
Sun 9am-9pm

Gluten FREE

BEANS AVAILABLE INSTORE

WIFI

CYCLE FRIENDLY

OUTDOOR SEATING

BRING YOUR OWN CUP

DOG FRIENDLY

www.nooknc.co.uk   T: 01614 325385
f @thenooknc   🐦 @thenooknc   📷 @thenooknc

MAP №68 COMMON GROUND

20 Shaw's Road, Altrincham, Cheshire, WA14 1QU

New owners Julie and Damian Besbrode wasted no time in making their mark on this Altrincham coffee shop when they took over in 2018. The duo not only doubled the space in which to slurp expertly extracted coffee, they also introduced a private meeting room and broadened the menu.

The team's informal approach to speciality coffee makes Common Ground a welcoming spot for both grinder gurus and newbie brewers. Whether you add sugar or prefer to go black, no eyebrows will be raised over your order.

INSIDER'S TIP LIKE WHAT YOU'RE LISTENING TO? DOWNLOAD COMMON GROUND'S PLAYLIST ON SPOTIFY

London roastery Caravan provides the beans of choice, expertly crafted to suit both espresso and filter. The baristas are happy to share the latest tasting notes and their thoughts on the most appropriate serve style.

If you're keen to make a meal of your visit, take a Scandi-chic seat and peruse the veggie and gluten-free-friendly menu – you'd be mad to miss out on a slice of the raw vegan cake.

ESTABLISHED
2017

KEY ROASTER
Caravan
Coffee Roasters

BREWING METHOD
Espresso,
AeroPress, V60,
batch brew,
cold brew

MACHINE
Victoria Arduino
Black Eagle

GRINDER
Victoria Arduino
Mythos One

OPENING HOURS
Mon-Fri 8am-5pm
Sat 9am-5pm
Sun 10am-5pm

www.commongroundalt.co.uk   T: 01619 416944
f @commongroundalt   🐦 @commongroundalt   📷 @commongroundalt

№69 BLANCHFLOWER BAKERY & KITCHEN

12-14 Shaw's Road, Altrincham, WA14 1QU

Blanchflower's Instagram feed really ought to come with an advisory caution, as once you start scrolling through the drool-inducing images there's no stopping until you reach the end – or throw in the towel and pay the bakery a visit.

You can't blame the team at the Altrincham bakery and kitchen for filling their grid with such deliciousness. When you're creating food this good, you'd be mad not to give it the glory it deserves. Everything on the creative menu is made from scratch, including the sourdough bread and baked beauties on the counter.

INSIDER'S TIP ROUND UP FELLOW COFFEE LOVING CHUMS TO SHARE A LARGE CHEMEX

The only bit of outsourcing comes courtesy of pop-up evening collabs with local chefs and street-food projects.

Founders Phil and Claire Howells started out by launching Caffeine and Co in Stretford in 2011 and they know coffee as well as they know food. The single origin espresso is roasted in Berlin by Five Elephant, while guest beans make the journey from Origin in Cornwall.

ESTABLISHED
2017

KEY ROASTER
Five Elephant

BREWING METHOD
Espresso, V60,
Kalita Wave

MACHINE
La Marzocco
Linea PB

GRINDER
Mythos 2,
Mahlkonig EK43

OPENING HOURS
Mon-Fri 9am-4.30pm
Sat 9am-5pm
Sun 9.30am-5pm

 Gluten FREE

 BEANS AVAILABLE INSTORE

 WIFI

 OUTDOOR SEATING

 DISABLED ACCESS

 DOG FRIENDLY

---

www.blanchflower.co.uk **T:** 01619 296724

f @blanchfloweralty **◎** @tblanchfloweralty

MAP № 70 TWO BROTHERS COFFEE

53 Stamford New Road, Altrincham, Cheshire, WA14 1DS

Determined to take the speciality coffee served at their Altrincham venue to the next level, brothers Dave and Steve took the roasting operation in-house at the start of 2019 and set up a micro-roastery in the basement.

Beans destined for Two Brothers' custom Sanremo Opera machine are now roasted in small batches downstairs alongside a seasonally changing line-up of single origins which the baristas experiment with on the brew bar. So whether you go espresso, V60 or batch brew, your coffee is guaranteed to be super fresh.

INSIDER'S TIP ASK NICELY AND THE TEAM MAY GIVE YOU A QUICK TOUR OF THE BASEMENT ROASTERY

Coffee engineers by choice, electrical engineers by trade, the brothers' backgrounds in the industry are referenced throughout the cafe's sleek interior: spot filament bulbs above the tables, electrical sketches on the walls and a bookshelf full of engineering literature.

The own-roasted coffee and personalised styling make this a unique spot to tuck in to a lazy brunch of smoked salmon and poached eggs or an afternoon cappuccino and cake session.

ESTABLISHED
2017

KEY ROASTER
Two Brothers Coffee

BREWING METHOD
Espresso, V60, batch brew

MACHINE
Sanremo Opera

GRINDER
Mythos One Clima Pro x 2, Mahlkonig EK43

OPENING HOURS
Mon-Fri 7am-5pm
Sat 8am-5pm
Sun 9.30am-4pm

 Gluten FREE
 BEANS AVAILABLE INSTORE
 WIFI
 CYCLE FRIENDLY
 OUTDOOR SEATING
 DISABLED ACCESS
 BRING YOUR OWN CUP
 COFFEE COURSES

www.twobrothers.coffee T: 01616 131821
f @twobrotherscoffeeltd @twobrothers_alt @twobrotherscoffee

MAP №71 LITTLE YELLOW PIG

31 Westminster Road, Hoole, Chester, Cheshire, CH2 3AX

From the vinyl memorabilia and comic books to the pig-themed art and Lego figurines, there's something to make even the most serious coffee drinker smile at this vibrant Chester meeting place.

In the middle of all these curios Little Yellow Pig founders Richard and Lucy craft grin-inducing brews using beans from London's Dark Arts. Pair the house-blend flat white with a wedge of homemade cake (the banana, dark choc and pecan loaf is addictive) and you'll be in caffeinated carby bliss.

INSIDER'S tip LITTLE YELLOW PIG 2.0 IS COMING SOON: WATCH THIS SPACE

If you're looking for something more filling to accompany your filter coffee, the kitchen knocks up a mean avo and poached eggs. There are pancakes, smoothie bowls and other brunch dishes on the line-up too, though the lure of perfect poachies is too powerful for most to resist.

This is a super sociable spot so make yourself at home, enjoy the epic playlist and buddy up with the smiley staff and rabble of loyal locals.

ESTABLISHED
2014

KEY ROASTER
Dark Arts Coffee

BREWING METHOD
Espresso,
AeroPress

MACHINE
La Marzocco
Linea Classic

GRINDER
Mythos One

OPENING HOURS
Mon-Fri 9am-5pm
Sat 9am-4pm
Sun 10am-2pm

 Gluten FREE

 BEANS AVAILABLE IN STORE

 WIFI

 CYCLE FRIENDLY

 OUTDOOR SEATING

 BRING YOUR OWN CUP

 DOG FRIENDLY

T: 01244 637220

f @littleyellowpighoole 🐦 @littleyellowpig 📷 @littleyellowpig31

ATKINSONS

COFFEE ROASTERS

Lancaster Castle

OPENING X.MMXIX

MAP№ 72 SHORT + STOUT

3a Ermine Road, Hoole, Chester, Cheshire, CH2 3PN

When the hustle of Hoole just isn't working for you, take a two-minute detour from the town centre to the caffeinated haven of SHORT + STOUT.

This mini slice of Melbourne is an inspired neighbourhood brunch spot where you can sit back and sip a flat white while soaking up the friendly buzz.

Exceptional house beans from Ancoats are carefully prepared via espresso to show off the bright and juicy notes that arise from expert roasting. Regulars can switch things up with guest roasts from the likes of Shropshire's Hundred House. In fact, SHORT + STOUT's quality brews are proving so popular that a new basement seating area recently opened to meet the growing demand.

INSIDER'S tip POP-UP EVENING EVENTS AND KOMBUCHA BREWING CLASSES ARE IN THE PIPELINE

The food's certainly part of the attraction and the gloriously bouncy pancakes are a must. Go trad with the bacon and maple option or plump for the chocolate version topped with strawberries and spun-sugar fairy floss. Veggies and vegans are never short of quality choices either.

ESTABLISHED
2018

KEY ROASTER
Ancoats Coffee Co.

BREWING METHOD
Espresso, cold brew, batch brew

MACHINE
La Marzocco Linea PB

GRINDER
Mythos One Clima Pro, Mazzer Mini

OPENING HOURS
Mon-Fri 7.30am-5pm
Sat 9am-4pm
Sun 9.30am-2pm

 Gluten FREE
 BEANS AVAILABLE INSTORE
 WIFI
 BRING YOUR OWN Cup
 DOG FRIENDLY

T: 01244 343378
f @SHORT + STOUT 🐦 @shortandstout_ 📷 @shortandstoutltd

MAP 73 JAUNTY GOAT COFFEE – 128

128 Northgate Street, Chester, Cheshire, CH1 2HT

Interest in plant-based eating has been the catalyst for an explosion of exciting new openings this year – including this much-anticipated second venue from Jaunty Goat.

While similar cafes have introduced the wider public to the delicious possibilities of vegan cuisine, few are as committed to pairing it with quality coffee as 128. Speciality beans, roasted specifically for Jaunty Goat, are delivered to the cafe numerous times each week, while guest coffees for espresso and filter are sourced from some of Europe's leading roasteries.

INSIDER'S tip IN SUMMER, SWAP ESPRESSO FOR A HOMEMADE COLD BREW TONIC

Alt milks from Minor Figures, Oatly and Bonsoy have been selected for their quality and capacity to be perfectly steamed to pair with espresso. Order a flattie, head to the outdoor seating area and find out for yourself – pair it with a slice of lemon and poppy seed cake, just to be safe.

If you're dabbling in flexitarianism, the reworked menu of classic brunch dishes won't disappoint. Try the full English with avocado, roasted vine tomatoes and homemade baked beans.

ESTABLISHED
2019

KEY ROASTER
Jaunty Goat
Coffee

BREWING METHOD
Espresso,
AeroPress,
V60, Chemex,
cold brew

MACHINE
Sanremo
Zoe Vision

GRINDER
Mazzer Robur,
Mazzer Major,
Mazzer ZM,
Mazzer Super
Jolly

OPENING HOURS
Mon-Sat **8**am-**6**pm
Sun **9**am-**6**pm

---

www.jauntygoatcoffee.co.uk   T: 01244 421492

f @jauntygoat   @jaunty_goat   @jaunty_goat

MAP 74 BEAN & COLE

41 Frodsham Street, Chester, Cheshire, CH1 3JJ

Domino sets, a cracking soundtrack and two resident spaniels make this the kind of cafe where you pop in for a quick coffee and find yourself still there three hours later.

The home-from-home atmosphere encourages loyal locals to kick back and order another drink from an ever-changing coffee line-up of interesting beans. Faves include Kiss the Hippo, Round Hill and Girls Who Grind, alongside house roaster Hasbean.

Like many cafe owners inspired by time spent in Australia, Nicole and Ian McArdle are single origin enthusiasts and, keen to share the love, host regular cupping sessions.

INSIDER'S TIP SOCIABLE POOCHES ARE WELCOME AT THIS DOG-FRIENDLY SPOT

Top-notch coffee, along with smoothie bowls, delicious cakes (many vegan and gluten free), muddy chai and the famous banana toast, have helped this Frodsham Street newbie scoop silver for Best Cafe and bronze for Best Newcomer in the Taste Cheshire Food and Drink Awards.

ESTABLISHED
2018

KEY ROASTER
Hasbean

BREWING METHOD
Espresso,
Chemex, V60,
AeroPress,
cold brew

MACHINE
Victoria Arduino
White Eagle T3

GRINDER
Nuova Simonelli
Mythos One x 2,
Mahlkonig EK43

OPENING HOURS
Mon-Fri **8.30**am-**5**pm
Sat **9**am-**5.30**pm
Sun **10**am-**4**pm

 Gluten FREE
 BEANS AVAILABLE INSTORE
 WIFI
 CYCLE FRIENDLY
 BRING YOUR OWN CUP
 DOG FRIENDLY

T: 01244 639060

 f @bean & cole   🐦 @beancolecoffee   📷 @beanandcolecoffee

MAP №75 CHALK COFFEE
24 Watergate Street, Chester, Cheshire, CH1 2LA

Blending uber-modern minimalism with the exposed bricks and arched ceilings of its historic setting, Chalk is a feast for both the eyes and the palate.

The speciality cafe is housed in one of Watergate Street's cavernous ground-floor shops where it lures in local coffee lovers and speciality-tuned tourists for quality coffee and artisan eats. When it's lashing down outside, venture into its depths and forget the real world for a while in favour of a good book, a flat white and a raspberry bakewell slice.

INSIDER'S TIP DITCHED DAIRY? CHOOSE BETWEEN OATLY AND BONSOY FOR YOUR FLATTIE

An imposing concrete bar at the centre of the action hosts seasonal coffee beans from Origin in Cornwall. The espresso menu is split into 'black' and 'with milk', and there are also batch brew options of the hot and iced varieties. If you're inspired to get brewing at home, you'll also discover a decent selection of beans – fresh from the roastery – on the retail shelves.

Lunch options are as pleasingly pared-back and on-point as the decor: choose from a handful of freshly prepped sandwich combos and follow with a wedge of brownie.

ESTABLISHED
2018

KEY ROASTER
Origin Coffee Roasters

BREWING METHOD
Espresso, batch brew

MACHINE
Victoria Arduino Black Eagle Gravimetric

GRINDER
Victoria Arduino Mythos One, Mahlkonig EK43

OPENING HOURS
Mon-Sat 8am-6pm
Sun 9am-6pm

www.chalkcoffee.co.uk   T: 01244 343345
f @chalkcoffee   🐦 @chalkcoffeeco   📷 @chalkcoffee

MAP №76 PANNA

35 Watergate Street, Chester, Cheshire, CH1 2LB

P anna was an early proponent of speciality coffee in Liverpool's business district and this sister outpost has taken the good vibes (and good coffee) to the centre of Chester.

The new hangout is housed in a Grade II-listed building and visitors can escape the bustle of the city by retiring to the cafe garden to sip their brew surrounded by Roman artefacts.

INSIDER'S TIP: SWITCHING UP THE ESPRESSO? COLD BREW AND COLD DRIP HIT THE MARK

Choose a single origin from Stafford's Hasbean or Panna's velvety house blend Smooth Criminal.

There are lots of options when it comes to serve style as the baristas have plenty of kit at their disposal – from the gleaming Victoria Arduino White Eagle through AeroPress and syphon to Chemex and V60.

Travel-inspired food features breakfast toasts such as mozzarella melted over prosciutto, Mexican brunches and Scandi-style coffee-and-cake combos.

ESTABLISHED
2013

KEY ROASTER
Hasbean

BREWING METHOD
Espresso,
AeroPress,
Chemex, V60,
syphon, cold
brew, cold drip

MACHINE
Victoria Arduino
White Eagle

GRINDER
Mahlkonig Vario,
Mythos One,
La Spaziale

OPENING HOURS
Mon-Sun 9am-5.30pm

Gluten FREE

BEANS AVAILABLE
INSTORE

WIFI

OUTDOOR SEATING

BRING YOUR OWN Cup

COFFEE COURSES

www.pannaliverpool.com   T: 01244 344553

f @pannacoffeechester   🐦 @panna_coffee   📷 @panna_coffee

MAP № 77 JAUNTY GOAT COFFEE – 57

57 Bridge Street, Chester, Cheshire, CH1 1NG

This Chester coffee shop may be housed in one of the city's historic Tudor Rows, yet the thoroughly photographable interiors and caffeine alchemy going down inside are peak 2019.

Behind the bar, baristas use bespoke house beans to craft Insta-ready latte art, pour whistle-clean filters and lavish ice with homemade cold brew. They also work their magic on guest roasts from the likes of Bonanza, Clifton and Square Mile, as well as loose-leaf teas and speciality hot chocolate.

INSIDER'S TIP PICK UP A BAG OF THE JAUNTY GOAT HOUSE ROAST ON YOUR WAY OUT

Take your pick of the drinks bill then grab a sunny spot in the window to mull over the concise menu of seasonal food. The chefs strive to keep the line-up humble and local – popular dishes include shakshuka with poached eggs and salsa verde, as well as brunch staples such as avocado on toast.

A recent reshuffle of the cafe space has made way for extra seating, more houseplants and some sleek new wooden tables which build on the pared-back Scandi vibe.

ESTABLISHED
2015

KEY ROASTER
Jaunty Goat
Coffee

BREWING METHOD
Espresso,
AeroPress,
V60, Chemex,
cold brew

MACHINE
Sanremo Opera

GRINDER
Mazzer Robur,
Mazzer Major,
Mazzer ZM,
Mazzer Super
Jolly

OPENING HOURS
Mon-Sat 8am-6pm
Sun 9am-6pm

www.jauntygoatcoffee.co.uk   T: 01244 421492

f @jauntygoat   🐦 @jaunty_goat   📷 @jaunty_goat

MAP №78 OBSCURE COFFEE

66 Lower Bridge Street, Chester, Cheshire, CH1 1RU

Take just a quick glance at this slick set-up on busy Lower Bridge Street and you could easily mistake it for a trendy speakeasy bar.

Look a little closer, however, and you'll discover that, amid the charcoal walls, dark wood furniture and pendant lighting, a sleek La Marzocco machine and sunshine yellow coffee cups take the place of martini glasses and boston shakers.

INSIDER'S tip MAKE SURE TO CHECK OUT THE BATHROOM – IT'S SUPER FANCY

Obscure may not serve intricate cocktails, but the same level of dedication and skill goes into its short bill of coffee based drinks. Founder Nick Wells (ex Brew Lab and Artisan Roast barista) works closely with Climpson & Sons which stocks the bar with seasonal beans. Prep styles include espresso, batch brew and V60.

Food is limited to a daily curation of cakes and pastries, but hey, you're probably not visiting with brunch in mind. Pick up a slice of salted caramel brownie, order a filter and head to the not-so-secret backroom for an off-grid coffee break.

ESTABLISHED
2018

KEY ROASTER
Climpson
& Sons

BREWING METHOD
Espresso, V60,
batch brew

MACHINE
La Marzocco
Linea·PB

GRINDER
Mahlkonig E65S,
Mahlkonig EK43 S

OPENING HOURS
Mon-Sat 9am-5pm
Sun 9am-4pm

Gluten FREE

BEANS AVAILABLE INSTORE

WIFI

BRING YOUR OWN Cup.

DOG FRIENDLY

🐦 @obscurecoffee   📷 @obscurecoffee

79 GRINDSMITH COFFEE ROASTERS

Unit 6, Varley Business Centre, Manchester, M40 8EL

It's been a busy first year at the Ancoats roastery for the Grindsmith gang. Since moving in to their high-spec lab in 2018, the team have refined their roasting skills, celebrated three Q grader qualifications and travelled to Colombia to strengthen relationships with the farmers who supply their greens.

In a short space of time they've achieved great things, thanks in part to their 'consistency is key' approach which ensures that every bag of beans is exceptional. The process begins with data-driven roasting, where density and moisture measurements are closely analysed, before rigorous cupping sessions call on human senses to quality-control every batch.

"A 'CONSISTENCY IS KEY" APPROACH ENSURES EVERY BAG IS EXCEPTIONAL"

A revolving list of five different roasts makes up the Grindsmith roster, and includes the house espresso blend Sixth Day which yields delicious brown sugar notes and raisin-like sweetness. As well as supplying its three venues in the city, Grindsmith beans pop up on guest grinders across Manchester and beyond.

ESTABLISHED
2018

ROASTER
MAKE & SIZE
Loring S15
Falcon 15kg

www.grindsmith.com   01614 084699

@grindsmith   @grindsmiths   @grindsmithcoffee

141

MAP №80 EXTRACT COFFEE ROASTERS

ECR Northern HQ, Spinningfields, Manchester

This pioneering roastery has stocked venues and trained baristas across northern England for years, so choosing Manchester for its first bricks-and-mortar training space outside of London or the Bristol HQ was a no-brainer.

Experienced barista and regional manager Jack Dobby heads up this new operation in Spinningfields. However, he's usually on the road, sharing his expert knowledge and giving Extract customers tailored training to help them get the best out of their ethically sourced beans.

ESTABLISHED
2019

COFFEE COURSES

COURSES

BEANS AVAILABLE
ONLINE

'POWER-UP SESSIONS FOCUS ON SPECIFIC ASPECTS OF COFFEE SERVICE'

Extract offers free foundation and intermediate barista training to all customers, while seasoned coffeesmiths can access the Power-Up Sessions which focus on specific aspects of service.

This year Jack and the team will also be working with local charities to support community projects based in the North.

---

www.extractcoffee.co.uk   T: 01179 554976

f @extractcoffeeroasters   🐦 @extractcoffee   📷 @extractcoffee

№102
Bloomfield Square

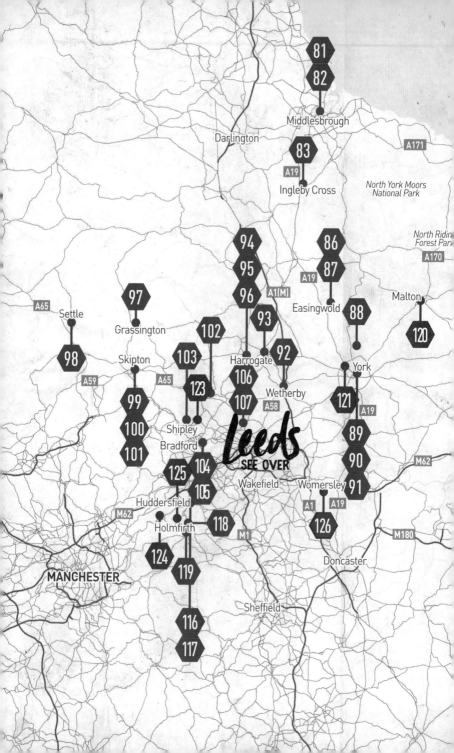

Locations are approximate

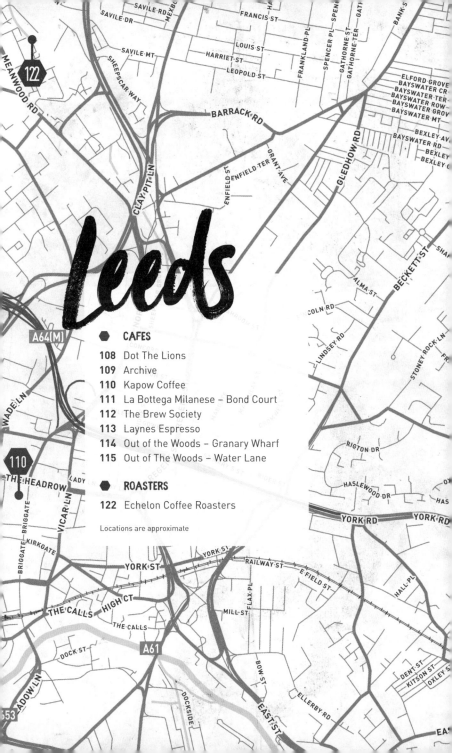

Leeds

Locations are approximate

ᴹᴬᴾ **81** OFF THE GROUND

63 Grange Road, Middlesbrough, North Yorkshire, TS1 5AS

Providing pick-me-ups since 2017, Off The Ground's delicious food offering and killer Origin house espresso guarantee customers a revitalising lift.

Sustainable and transparent sourcing is the foundation upon which the business was built, so the Cornish roastery's ethical approach to coffee fits nicely. As a social enterprise, Off The Ground's work with the community is important and projects have included local fundraisers and hosting mental health and drug rehab support groups.

INSIDER'S TIP A NEW OUTDOOR SEATING SPACE WILL BE READY IN SPRING 2020

For those who choose to support the team's mission with a visit to the chipboard-chic cafe, opting for a vegan-friendly grain bowl piled high with colourful veggies is a good start. Sound too virtuous? A mega slab of Songbird Bakery's salted caramel brownie should restore your status quo.

The glass-fronted space has a laid-back and friendly vibe – stick around to sample the latest guest from the likes of North Star, Bailies and Girls Who Grind, and get the low-down on the next grassroots initiative being supported by the Off The Ground team.

ESTABLISHED
2017

KEY ROASTER
Origin Coffee Roasters

BREWING METHOD
Espresso, V60, AeroPress

MACHINE
La Marzocco Linea PB

GRINDER
Victoria Arduino Mythos One

OPENING HOURS
Mon-Fri 9am-5.30pm
Sat 10am-5.30pm
Sun 11.30am-4pm

Gluten FREE

BEANS AVAILABLE / INSTORE

WIFI

CYCLE FRIENDLY

DISABLED ACCESS

BRING YOUR OWN Cup

DOG FRIENDLY

---

www.offthegroundcoffee.co.uk T: 07803 090476

f @offthegrounduk   🐦 @offthegrounduk   📷 @offthegrounduk

ᴹᴬᴾ'ˢ 82 BEDFORD ST COFFEE

27 Bedford Street, Middlesbrough, North Yorkshire, TS1 2LL

Middlesbrough's flourishing food and drink quarter is shaped by the spirit of its independent traders and at its centre you'll find the Bedford team, flying the flag for quality coffee and wholesome grub.

This is the first cafe from local indie Rounton and, other than rocking up at the roastery, it's the best place to drink the coffee exactly how the roasters intended. The latest own-roasted blends and single origins are all available to try at the counter, but the team aren't precious and also love sharing beans they've picked up on their travels. Recent finds have included Berlin's Fjord and Tweed from Texas.

INSIDER'S TIP: BE THE FIRST TO TRY NEW ROASTS FROM ROUNTON AT THE CUPPING EVENTS

Despite the distinctly urban red brick and black wood interior, the new menu takes a rustic approach to brunch and afternoon pick-me-ups. Visit for doorstep slices of locally baked granary bread with tasty toppings (the eggs benny with 12-hour-roasted pork is particularly tempting) as well as generous hunks of homemade cake.

ESTABLISHED
2015

KEY ROASTER
Rounton Coffee
Roasters

BREWING METHOD
Espresso, V60,
AeroPress,
batch filter

MACHINE
Sanremo
Verona RS

GRINDER
Mahlkonig EK43,
Mahlkonig E65S

OPENING HOURS
Mon-Fri **8**am-**4**pm
Sat **9**am-**4**pm
Sun **10**am-**3**pm

www.rountoncoffee.co.uk T: 01642 647856

f @bedfordstcoffee @ @bedfordstcoffee

№83 THE JOINERS SHOP

Cross Lane, Ingleby Cross, Northallerton, North Yorkshire, DL6 3ND

You know you've struck liquid gold when the coffee you're sipping comes from beans bronzed just down the road, which are in the hopper within days of being roasted.

This Northallerton indie may be a little off the beaten track, but the rural gem is worth making a diversion for. Visit for the homemade food and friendly welcome as well as the fresher-than-fresh beans.

INSIDER'S TIP POOCHES ARE TREATED TO PUPCAKES AND WATER

With an open-plan kitchen, a contemporary cafe space and gorgeous views over a tumbling landscape, this is a cool spot to sip great coffee and sink your teeth in to one of the homemade bakes after a stroll over the hills.

Thanks to the cafe's location on Wainwright's winding Coast to Coast path, it's also a haunt of serious hikers who stop off to rest their legs and recharge with an award winning brekkie before continuing the trail.

Up for something stronger? The venue is the owner of a shiny new drinks licence.

ESTABLISHED
2017

KEY ROASTER
Rounton Coffee Roasters

BREWING METHOD
Espresso

MACHINE
Sanremo Verona RS

GRINDER
Mahlkonig K30

OPENING HOURS
Mon-Sat 9.30am-4pm
Sun 10am-4pm

www.rountoncoffee.co.uk   T: 01609 882762

f @thejoinersshop   🐦 @thejoinersshop   📷 @thejoinersshop

№84 GREENSMITH

30 St Nicholas Street, Scarborough, North Yorkshire, YO11 2HF

Come Friday night, the baristas at this minimalist venue off Scarborough's main drag dim the industrial lighting, turn up the funky playlist and swap tampers for cocktail shakers.

There's a continental approach to cafe culture at Greensmith: late weekend opening hours and a list of boozy specials blur the line between coffee shop and bar. Don't be surprised if your table neighbours are sipping afternoon Espresso Martinis while you tuck in to a still-hot-from-the-oven pastel de nata and nitro cold brew.

INSIDER'S TIP: THE SHOP USED TO BE A GENTLEMEN'S OUTFITTERS – SPOT THE ORIGINAL GOLD LEAF SIGNAGE

Whether you're drinking from a cup or a coupe glass, the house espresso is roasted by Dark Woods. The Huddersfield indie also stumps up a single origin for V60, while North Star provides a Rwandan decaf espresso.

One of the original speciality shops in the seaside town, the cafe also hosts an annual latte art throwdown for local baristas – and team Greensmith are reigning champs two years and counting, natch.

ESTABLISHED
2014

KEY ROASTER
Dark Woods
Coffee

BREWING METHOD
Espresso,
batch filter,
nitro cold brew

MACHINE
Cimbali M100

GRINDER
Anfim SP II,
Cimbali Magnum

OPENING HOURS
Mon-Thu 9am-5pm
Fri-Sat 9am-9pm

Gluten FREE

BEANS AVAILABLE INSTORE

DISABLED ACCESS

DOG FRIENDLY

MAP № 85 YAY COFFEE!

Woodend Creative, The Crescent, Scarborough, North Yorkshire, YO11 2PW

Yay has found its perfect location inside the historic Italianate villa that is home to the Woodend Creative crew. It's a meeting of minds and tastebuds with an arty bunch who share the same love of culture and coffee.

The Yay team cultivate a welcoming atmosphere and their excitement about the coffee they brew is infectious. A kaleidoscope of flavours from the house Extract beans are tickled out via Chemex, AeroPress, V60 and Clever Dripper.

Alternatively, take a barista recommendation from the ever-rotating menu of single origins to discover something different from Has Bean, Workshop or Square Mile. Loose teas served in ingenuiTEA pots will tempt leaf lovers.

INSIDER'S TIP SNEAK OUTSIDE TO SAVOUR YOUR BREW IN THE LEAFY GARDEN

Bakes – both savoury and sweet – are created in-house and include deep-filled tarts (try the mushroom and gruyère) alongside rather indulgent cakes. The chocolate and raspberry is a sure crowd-pleaser, but constant experimentation means there's no shortage of new things to sample.

ESTABLISHED
2015

KEY ROASTER
Extract Coffee Roasters

BREWING METHOD
Espresso, V60, AeroPress, Clever Dripper, Chemex

MACHINE
La Marzocco Linea PB

GRINDER
Nuova Simonelli Mythos One, Mahlkonig EK43

OPENING HOURS
Tue-Sat 9am-5pm

www.yaycoffee.com   T: 01723 364133

f @yaycoffeeuk   🐦 @yaycoffeeuk   📷 @yaycoffeeuk

№86 TEAHEE! ESPRESSO BAR

Old Toll Booth, 3 Market Place, Easingwold, York, North Yorkshire, YO61 3AB

A former toll keeper's cottage isn't an obvious place to find speciality coffee but hey, we'll take a drop of the good stuff wherever it's brewed.

Leeds' North Star keeps the hopper humming with its expertly roasted beans and enables the skilled baristas to craft flavour-popping brews.

Currently Teahee! favours the roastery's Czar Street Seasonal Blend as the house choice for espresso due to its delicious flavour profile of blackberry, dark chocolate and orange.

INSIDER'S TIP CAFFEINE OVERKILL? TREAT YOURSELF TO ONE OF THE LOOSE-LEAF TEAS

This Easingwold haunt isn't just a find for its seriously good coffee either; unctuous slabs of award winning homemade cake are also available to be paired with your cup of choice. Signature bakes include a lemon and almond drizzle, three-seed and honey flapjack, and lip-lickingly good Tunisian orange cake.

Stick around for lunch and enjoy seasonally led healthy dishes or, if the sun's playing ball, feast alfresco in the leafy courtyard garden.

ESTABLISHED
2003

KEY ROASTER
North Star
Coffee Roasters

BREWING METHOD
Espresso,
french press

MACHINE
Sanremo
Verona RS

GRINDER
Mahlkonig K30,
Mazzer Mini

OPENING HOURS
Mon-Sat 8am-4pm
Sun 10am-3pm

T: 01347 823533
f @teahees 🐦 @teahee 📷 @teahee.easingwold

MAP № 87 THE CURIOUS TABLE

Market Place, Easingwold, York, North Yorkshire, YO61 3AG

The scent of freshly baked brownies and just-pulled espresso lures passersby into this Easingwold institution. It's a hard-to-resist combo, especially when the heavenly slabs of chocolatey bake are laden with extra goodies such as molten caramel and peanut butter.

The bespoke house blend from nearby York Emporium is the pleasing partner, its nutty notes drawn from a marriage of fairly traded beans from Vietnam, Ethiopia, Brazil and Guatemala. Plump for your regular coffee order or try the split shot (one served as espresso, one as filter) and compare the coffee's flavours with and without milk.

INSIDER'S TIP — EACH BREW COMES WITH A BITE-SIZED CHUNK OF BROWNIE

While The Curious Table's cake counter is almost impossible to swerve, it's worth holding out on indulgence until you've done brunch. The new menu includes an unmissable french toast showered in fruity toppings.

Beyond the daily thrills, the cafe also hosts pop-up evenings in collaboration with local chefs – keep an eye on social for news and dates.

ESTABLISHED
2013

KEY ROASTER
York Coffee Emporium

BREWING METHOD
Espresso, AeroPress, french press

MACHINE
Cimbali

GRINDER
Cimbali Magnum

OPENING HOURS
Mon-Fri 7.30am-5pm
Sat 8.30am-4pm
Sun 9.30am-3pm

www.thecurioustable.co.uk   T: 01347 823434

f @thecurioustable   🐦 @thecurioustable   📷 @curious.table

MAP №88 THE CURIOUS COFFEE COMPANY

Unit 8, Haxby Shopping Centre, Haxby, York, North Yorkshire, YO32 2LU

This second instalment of the Curious chronicles followed four years after the launch of the original Curious Table cafe in Easingwold. It was an eagerly anticipated sequel for the Company's loyal following of caffeine fans.

Just like its big sister, the Haxby hangout uses a bespoke York Coffee Emporium blend which is brewed via espresso or french press. Regular training sessions at the roastery ensure the baristas' skills are bang up to date and guarantee a quality cup every time.

INSIDER'S TIP — TRY ONE OF THE CHOCOLATE 'SCOTCH EGGS'

Whatever you plump for, a tempting hunk of homemade brownie accompanies every hot drink. And once you've munched that gooey square, it's more than likely you'll make a return trip to the counter to upgrade to a full-sized piece or a wedge of Oreo millionaire traycake.

Regular pizza nights add a buzzy community vibe to the cool suburban spot. Owners Eddie and Jenny Copley-Farnell take charge of the oven and turn out drool-worthy combos such as The Tree Hugger which deals in barbecued pulled jackfruit, red onion, mozzarella and rocket.

ESTABLISHED
2017

KEY ROASTER
York Coffee Emporium

BREWING METHOD
Espresso, french press

MACHINE
Cimbali M39

GRINDER
Faema MD3000

OPENING HOURS
Mon-Fri 7.30am-5pm
Sat 8.30am-4pm
Sun 9.30am-3pm

Gluten FREE

BEANS AVAILABLE — INSTORE

WIFI

CYCLE FRIENDLY

OUTDOOR SEATING

DISABLED ACCESS

BRING YOUR OWN CUP

COFFEE COURSES

DOG FRIENDLY

---

www.curiouscoffee.co T: 01904 765158

f @thecuriouscoffeecompany @curiouscoffeeed @thecuriouscoffeecompany

MAP№89 SPRING ESPRESSO – LENDAL

21 Lendal, York, North Yorkshire, YO1 8AQ

A stroll across the river from the train station into the thrumming heart of York brings visitors to Spring Espresso's inviting facade.

The entrance is flower-festooned, the huge windows yield an enticing array of cakes and the toasty-nutty scent of freshly ground coffee wafts from the front door each time it swings open.

It may sound rather halcyon but caffeine is serious business here, with a Synesso Hydra MVP in the hands of skilled baristas who use pressure profiling to extract the very finest flavours.

INSIDER'S TIP TRY AN EIGHT-HOUR COLD BREW OVER ICE WITH A DASH OF TONIC

House beans come from Coffeesmiths, where they've been bespoke-roasted to Spring's exacting specifications. Guest backup is capably handled by Small Batch, so whatever you choose from the brew bar you're assured of a first-rate cup.

Resisting the blueberry or bacon and pecan pancake stacks is futile (don't bother trying) while elegantly decorated bakes provide yet further temptation.

ESTABLISHED
2016

KEY ROASTER
Coffeesmiths Collective

BREWING METHOD
Espresso, V60, AeroPress, cold brew

MACHINE
Synesso Hydra MVP

GRINDER
Victoria Arduino Mythos One Clima Pro, Mahlkonig EK43

OPENING HOURS
Mon-Sun 8am-6pm

www.springespresso.co.uk   T: 01904 656556

f @springespressolendal   🐦 @springespresso   📷 @springespresso

ᴹᴬᴾ№ 90 SPRING ESPRESSO – FOSSGATE

45 Fossgate, York, North Yorkshire, YO1 9TF

York's historic Merchant Quarter is where the flagship Spring Espresso calls home. It's a thriving area with a rep for game-changing indie businesses – and where thirsty locals head for exceptional brews.

Spring Espresso founders Steve and Tracey Dyson collaborated with the roasting maestros at Coffeesmiths to create their bespoke seasonal blend (you won't taste it anywhere else). Guest roasts from Small Batch take a supporting role and can be sampled in your favourite espresso based choice or as V60 or AeroPress.

INSIDER'S Tip ATTENTION VEGANS! NEW PLANT-BASED MENU OPTIONS INCOMING

Whatever the serve style, you'll be impressed by the talent (and friendliness) of the barista team. Steve is a UKBC sensory judge and has passed on his sharpened palate and eye for faultless latte art to the team.

When you're against the clock, nip in for a posh bacon sandwich and a speedy flattie. Otherwise, linger over the avo eggs, pancake stack or epic slice of Bostock (a kind of baked French toast) and do the experience justice.

ESTABLISHED
2011

KEY ROASTER
Coffeesmiths Collective

BREWING METHOD
Espresso, V60, AeroPress, cold brew

MACHINE
Synesso Hydra

GRINDER
Victoria Arduino Mythos One, Mahlkonig EK43 S

OPENING HOURS
Mon-Sun 8am-6pm

www.springespresso.co.uk   T: 01904 627730

f @springespressofossgate   🐦 @springespresso   📷 @springespresso

MAP № 91 BISON COFFEE HOUSE

17 Heslington Road, York, North Yorkshire, YO10 5AR

The team at this York coffee house like to keep regulars on their toes, eschewing a house roast in favour of Hasbean single origins which are updated a couple of times each week.

'We want to showcase the wide variety of flavours that coffees from different corners of the world can yield,' explains co-owner Joe Walker.

INSIDER'S tip GET THE LOW-DOWN ON THE DAY'S COFFEE NOTES VIA THE CHALKBOARD

The result is that visitors to the compact coffee house always have something exciting and seasonal to sample via espresso. Nitro cold brew is also available, brewed overnight by the Bison team before being kegged up and ready for action at the bar.

There's not a huge amount of space in which to settle down with a brew, but if you can nab a seat among the quirky vintage decor and collection of souvenir spoons (niche but kinda cool) it's a cosy spot in which to spend an hour. A small menu of bagels and toasties (with plenty of vegan options) accompanies the coffee, and if you're looking for a quick thrill a slab of cookie-dough brownie is the way to go.

ESTABLISHED
2011

KEY ROASTER
Hasbean

BREWING METHOD
Espresso, nitro

MACHINE
Sanremo Capri

GRINDER
Sanremo SR50

OPENING HOURS
Mon-Fri 9am-5pm
Sat 10am-5pm
Sun 11am-4pm

www.bisoncoffee.co.uk   T: 01904 637607
f @bisoncoffeeyork   @ @bisonyork

MAP № 92 BOTTLE & BEAN

Unit 1, Church Street, Wetherby, West Yorkshire, LS22 6LP

Tired of travelling to Leeds to get a decent cup of coffee and fed up of pulling uninspiring pints at the local pub, Andy Levine decided to ditch the day job and set up his own hub of quality caffeine and craft beer in Wetherby.

Since taking on a small unit on Church Street in March 2018, Andy and partner Clair have gathered a loyal following of like-minded souls who share the pair's passion for good coffee, beer, art and music.

Inside the shop, four beer taps showcase local and international brewers, while endless rows of colourful craft ales are accompanied by Andy's own artwork. There's even a turntable so regulars can bring in vinyl and give it a spin as they sip.

INSIDER'S TIP A SELECTION OF 100 CRAFT BEERS MAKES LEAVING EMPTY-HANDED IMPOSSIBLE

Beans fuelling the friendly vibe are sourced from roasteries across the country. *'We try lots of coffees and change the line-up regularly,'* says Andy. *'Switching things up is a great way to introduce newbies to the subtleties of different beans.'*

ESTABLISHED
2018

KEY ROASTER
Multiple roasters

BREWING METHOD
Espresso, V60

MACHINE
Sanremo Zoe

GRINDER
Sanremo SR50 OD

OPENING HOURS
Tue-Wed **9.30**am-**3**pm
Thu-Sat **9.30**am-**6**pm

BEANS AVAILABLE INSTORE

WIFI

DISABLED ACCESS

BRING YOUR OWN CUP

DOG FRIENDLY

www.bottleandbeanwetherby.co.uk   T: 01937 587458

f @bottleandbeanwetherby   🐦 @bottle_and_bean   ⓞ @bottle_and_bean_wetherby

MAP 93 NUMBER THIRTEEN COFFEE HOUSE & CAKERY

13 Castlegate, Knaresborough, North Yorkshire, HG5 8AR

Like so many aspiring baristas, it was time spent living and working in New Zealand that pushed Sarah to take the plunge and open her own coffee shop.

Creating a cafe from scratch on a small budget is no mean feat, so Sarah enlisted the help of her friends and family to scour north Yorkshire's auctions, charity shops and garage sales to fill her new venture with retro cups, quirky furniture and funky fittings. The result of their combined bargain-hunting is a masterpiece of granny-chic – and a super cosy spot in which to hunker down with a good coffee and slice of homemade indulgence.

Sourcing sustainably and locally is at the heart of Number Thirteen. Roost in Malton bronzes the house blend while other Yorkshire roasters take turns on the guest V60 spot. The cafe even scooped a BusinessGreen Award for its ethical efforts within a year of opening.

ESTABLISHED
2018

KEY ROASTER
Roost Coffee
& Roastery

BREWING METHO
Espresso, V60

MACHINE
Rocket Espresso
Boxer

GRINDER
Expobar Zenith
On Demand

OPENING HOURS
Tue-Sat **8.30**am-4pm

INSIDER'S TIP MILK IS DELIVERED IN GLASS BOTTLES SO EVERY COFFEE IS PLASTIC-FREE

If you're in the area, look out for monthly BYO bistro nights and biannual Frock Exchange events where you can swap your preloved clothes with like-minded locals.

---

www.thirteencastlegate.com   T: 07725 578599

f @thirteencastlegate   🐦 @13castlegate   📷 @thirteencastlegate

≡ №94 BEAN & BUD

14 Commercial Street, Harrogate, North Yorkshire, HG1 1TY

osmopolitan couple Phil and Helen Dolby left a decade-long sojourn in Switzerland to take over this Harrogate stalwart in November 2018.

The pair were first smitten with speciality while travelling in New Zealand, and have been building on the cafe's USP of single origin beans that can be traced back to the farmer. You'd be forgiven for feeling like a child in a sweet shop when visiting their bright cosy cafe with its bonanza of beans. House roasters include Campbell & Syme, North Star, Maude and Round Hill, while there are also guest appearances from the likes of Origin and Outpost.

INSIDER'S TIP BE FIRST IN THE QUEUE FOR THE FRESHLY BAKED PASTEL DE NATA

Seasonal Latin American and African beans can be sipped as espresso or filter and there's always a decaf on the go. Tea is in equal abundance: choose from ethically sourced loose black, green, oolong and white leaves.

Pair your caffeinated pick of the chalkboard with a fresh pastry, Yorkshire skyr and granola or a chunky slice of hot buttered toast.

ESTABLISHED
2010

KEY ROASTER
Multiple roasters

BREWING METHOD
Espresso, V60, Chemex, AeroPress, Kalita Wave, batch brew

MACHINE
La Marzocco Strada EP

GRINDER
Mythos, Mahlkonig K30, Mahlkonig Tanzania

OPENING HOURS
Mon-Sat 8am-5pm
Sun 10am-4pm

www.beanandbud.co.uk
f @beanandbud 🐦 @beanandbud 📷 @beanandbud

MAP № 95 NO35 HARROGATE

35 Cheltenham Crescent, Harrogate, North Yorkshire, HG1 1DH

While the team at this Harrogate coffee shop take speciality pretty seriously, the recent appointment of Walter the cockerpoo as head of customer service suggests they also understand the importance of fun.

Walter usually fulfils his duties (greeting guests and begging for belly rubs) from the sunny bench in the front window before he hands over to the baristas behind the white-tiled bar. With a trio of pourover methods and a snazzy cream Sanremo machine at their disposal, they're poised to craft visitors something delicious.

North Star provides the house roast, while guest options come from the likes of Girls Who Grind, Maude and Craft House. Get up to speed on the latest tasting notes while giving Walter his tip in cuddles.

INSIDER'S TIP VEGANS! DON'T MISS OUT ON THE BAGELS – TRY THE AVO, ROCKET AND TOMATO MEDLEY

No35's cracking coffee is complemented by a daily line-up of freshly stuffed bagels. Tour the world on your lunchbreak with house faves such as the Mumbai (curried chicken, lettuce, mango chutney), New Yorker (gouda, pastrami, gherkins, mustard mayo) or Londoner (smashed avo, prosciutto, mayo).

ESTABLISHED
2017

KEY ROASTER
North Star
Coffee Roasters

BREWING METHOD
Espresso, V60,
Chemex,
AeroPress

MACHINE
Sanremo
Verona TCS

GRINDER
Sanremo
SR70 Evo

OPENING HOURS
Mon-Fri 7am-5pm
Sat 9am-5pm
Sun 10am-4pm

Gluten FREE
BEANS AVAILABLE
INSTORE
WIFI
CYCLE FRIENDLY
OUTDOOR seating
DISABLED ACCESS
BRING YOUR OWN Cup
DOG FRIENDLY

www.no35harrogate.coffee

f @No35Harrogate 🐦 @no35harrogate 📷 @no35harrogate

MAP №96 STARLING INDEPENDENT BEER & COFFEE HOUSE

47 Oxford Street, Harrogate, North Yorkshire, HG1 1PW

This Harrogate CAMRA Pub of the Year 2018, located in one of the spa town's oldest buildings, may look, at first glance, like an old-school boozer thanks to its beams, rafters and bare stone walls. However, on closer inspection, the dedicated coffee fan will soon sniff out that the flat whites are as good as the bitter.

Ethically sourced and attentively roasted beans for espresso come from Dark Woods in Huddersfield, with single origin guests on rotation for V60. The team aim to offer a wide range of flavour profiles to suit palates of all persuasions. If you fancy taking the reins and prepping your own pourover, the self-serve option comes complete with instructions.

INSIDER'S tip COOL OFF WITH CANNED NITRO COLD BREW FROM MINOR FIGURES

Food is served all day, with a comprehensive brunch menu catering for the peckish (porridge, granola) to the ravenous (chorizo and merguez hash hits the spot). Pizzas are handmade in the Neapolitan style, while poutine (cheese curds, hand-cut chips and beef gravy) offers a Yorkshire spin on the Canadian classic.

ESTABLISHED
2017

KEY ROASTER
Dark Woods
Coffee

BREWING METHOD
Espresso, V60

MACHINE
La Marzocco
Linea

GRINDER
Mazzer
Super Jolly,
Mahlkonig EK43

OPENING HOURS
Mon-Wed **9**am-**10**pm
Thu-Sat **9**am-**11**pm
Sun **10**am-**10**pm

Gluten FREE

BEANS AVAILABLE INSTORE

WIFI

BRING YOUR OWN Cup.

DOG FRIENDLY

www.starlinghgte.co.uk   T: 01423 531310
f @starlinghgte   🐦 @starlinghgte   📷 @starlinghgte

MAP№ 97 THE HEDGEROW

Station Road, Threshfield, North Yorkshire, BD23 5BP

Whether it's the waft of coffee or the fragrance of flowers that lures you in, you'll be happy to have stumbled upon The Hedgerow in the Dales village of Threshfield.

This florist and coffee shop is a fully family affair, run by Wendy and Nigel with their daughter Heather. Together they've created a bright and airy interior which invites customers to meander past tumbles of country-chic blooms on their way to the counter.

INSIDER'S TIP IN SUMMER, TAKE YOUR SIP OF CHOICE OUTDOORS AND BASK ON THE ALFRESCO SEATING AREA

Experienced horticulturist Nigel brought his green-fingered experience to the table in 2019, and since then The Hedgerow has grown to include a dedicated plant centre in the garden.

Heather is renowned for her brewing skills and her drinks menu is pleasingly pared-back, utilising beans from Atkinsons. Happily, the Lancaster roaster's dedication to 'relationship coffee' (which builds bonds between growers, cafes and espresso drinkers) makes perfect sense in this foliage and family-focused setting.

ESTABLISHED
1987

KEY ROASTER
Atkinsons
Coffee Roasters

BREWING METHOD
Espresso,
batch filter

MACHINE
Nuova Simonelli
Aurelia II

GRINDER
Nuova Simonelli
Mythos One

OPENING HOURS
Tue-Fri 8am-4.30pm
Sat 8am-3pm

Gluten FREE

BEANS AVAILABLE
INSTORE

WIFI

CYCLE FRIENDLY

OUTDOOR Seating

DISABLED ACCESS

BRING YOUR OWN Cup

DOG FRIENDLY

---

www.the-hedgerow.co.uk   T: 01765 752293
f @thehedgerowthreshfeild   @ @the_hedgerow

№98 LAY OF THE LAND

Kings Mill Lane, Settle, North Yorkshire, BD24 9BS

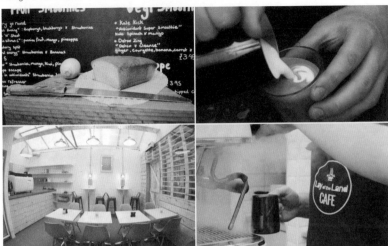

If you're charmed by the slightly unusual combo of quality flora and flatties, then Lay of the Land is a delicious find. You'll discover it in Settle's garden centre, where it cultivates some of the best coffee (and food) for miles.

Round off a potter around the plants with lunch at the greenhouse-esque space where James 'Jimmie' Lay leads a small team of enthusiastic baristas and chefs. Jimmie trained at Michelin starred Northcote in Langho and his menus bloom with interesting takes on traditional dishes.

INSIDER'S tip TUCK IN TO A HOT-FROM-THE-OVEN SAUSAGE ROLL WITH ROASTED GARLIC AND THYME

Everything from flatbreads to salsa is made from scratch in the tiny kitchen and there are plans afoot to start growing veggies in a kitchen garden. House favourites such as the huge slabs of quiche make the most of seasonal ingredients like wild garlic and cherry tomatoes.

The fantastic fodder is matched by single origin coffee from local roaster Casa Espresso. Beans are switched up every couple of weeks to reflect the seasonal harvest and there is a good selection of loose-leaf teas available too.

ESTABLISHED
2015

KEY ROASTER
Casa Espresso

BREWING METHOD
Espresso,
AeroPress,
pourover

MACHINE
Sanremo
Verona RS

GRINDER
Sanremo
SR70 Evo

OPENING HOURS
Mon-Sat 9am-4pm
Sun 10am-3pm

 Gluten FREE

 BEANS AVAILABLE INSTORE

 WIFI

 CYCLE FRIENDLY

 OUTDOOR seating

 DISABLED ACCESS

 BRING YOUR OWN cup

 DOG FRIENDLY

www.layoftheland.co.uk T: 01729 824247

f @layofthelandsettle 🐦 @lay_of_the_land 📷 @layoftheland_settle

ᴹᴬᴾ99 EXCHANGE COFFEE COMPANY – SKIPTON

10 Gargrave Road, Skipton, North Yorkshire, BD23 1PJ

Crossing the threshold at Exchange Coffee's Skipton branch with its delightful step-back-in-time vibe is guaranteed to charm any serious coffee lover.

The building has a deeply caffeinated history, having been a roastery long before the award winning Exchange brigade moved in. A deliciously retro atmosphere still pervades and oozes from wooden shelves lined with tea caddies, while the fragrance of freshly ground beans and tisanes envelops those sitting and sipping in the genteel Victorian-front-room cafe.

INSIDER'S TIP INVESTIGATE THE RETAIL SHELVES AND STOCK UP ON HOME BREWING MUST-HAVES

Modern innovation comes from the presence of the Probat GN12 which is hunkered down in the corner. Freshness is everything here and as you browse the mind-boggling selection of beans and teas (there are over 100) you'll also be treated to the toasty thrills of a roast in progress.

If you're drinking in, opt for syrupy espresso and its associated drinks or pick a single origin for Clever Dripper. However, if you're sitting in a high-backed chair nibbling tea bread against a backdrop of Arts and Crafts wallpaper, pushing down the plunger on a refined french press seems most apt.

ESTABLISHED
1997

KEY ROASTER
Exchange Coffee Company

BREWING METHOD
Espresso, Clever Dripper, french press

MACHINE
Expobar G10

GRINDER
Mahlkonig K30

OPENING HOURS
Mon-Sat 9am-4.30pm

---

www.exchangecoffee.co.uk   T: 01756 795649

f @exchangecoffeecompany   🐦 @exchange_coffee   📷 @exchange_coffee

№100 STEEP & FILTER

14 Otley Street, Skipton, North Yorkshire, BD23 1DZ

If you want to do your bit to save the planet, make use of all those empty Mason jars at the back of your cupboard and get a stonking coffee while you're at it, schedule a visit to Steep & Filter.

After taking advantage of the cafe's fantastic refill station (take along your empty containers and get your household shop done without leaving a mountain of rubbish in your wake), settle in for an espresso courtesy of North Star.

Your weekday reward will be the rich seasonal Czar Street blend, while #saturdaytakeover at the hopper is a chance to be adventurous and try the latest single origin from the Leeds roastery.

INSIDER'S tip GET UP TO SPEED ON ECO ISSUES AT THE REGULAR MEETINGS AND TALKS

Loose-leaf enthusiasts will be pleased to discover an equally specialist offering of fairly traded and single origin teas. Infusions include Taiwanese Tie Guan Yin yellow and Chinese Dian Hong black teas.

A plant-based menu of brunch dishes and lunchtime feasts continues the eco ethos. Chow down on the popular Hash & Scrambles, or tuck in to a bowl of steaming tarka dhal or veggie chilli.

ESTABLISHED
2018

KEY ROASTER
North Star
Coffee Roasters

BREWING METHOD
Espresso,
Moccamaster

MACHINE
La Marzocco
Linea PB

GRINDER
Fiorenzato
F64 Evo

OPENING HOURS
Mon, Wed-Sat
8am-4.30pm
Tue 8am-3.30pm
Sun 9am-3.30pm

Gluten FREE

BEANS AVAILABLE
INSTORE

WIFI

CYCLE FRIENDLY

DISABLED ACCESS

BRING YOUR OWN cup

DOG FRIENDLY

T: 01756 795797

f Steep&Filter 🐦 @steepandfilter 📷 @steepandfilter

№ 101 BEAN LOVED

17 Otley Street, Skipton, North Yorkshire, BD23 1DY

If you're a fan of Dark Woods' west Yorkshire roasted beans, you'll want to schedule a jaunt to this Skipton independent.

The team at Bean Loved go to great lengths to craft the perfect cup, making regular trips to Dark Woods HQ to ensure their signature house blend tastes lip-smackingly good.

All their hard work and diligence paid off in 2016 when the cafe was awarded exceptional accreditation by the Beverage Standards Association and was shortlisted for the Best Flat White in the UK award.

INSIDER'S TIP: QUENCH YOUR THIRST WITH A FRESHLY BLITZED SMOOTHIE BEFORE HITTING THE COFFEE

It's not just espresso that founder Wes Bond and head chef Alastair Fox are passionate about. A new menu has taken the food offering up another notch and visitors can now tuck in to creative compilations such as sweet potato fritters, shakshuka baked eggs and flatbread piled with mint-and-lemon-smashed peas. Whatever you choose, it's likely to be seasonal and locally sourced.

ESTABLISHED
2007

KEY ROASTER
Dark Woods Coffee

BREWING METHOD
Espresso

MACHINE
La Marzocco FB80

GRINDER
Nuova Simonelli Mythos One, Mahlkonig EK43

OPENING HOURS
Mon-Fri 7.30am-5pm
Sat 8am-5pm
Sun 9am-4pm

Gluten FREE

BEANS AVAILABLE INSTORE

WIFI

CYCLE FRIENDLY

OUTDOOR seating

DISABLED ACCESS

BRING YOUR OWN Cup

DOG FRIENDLY

www.beanloved.co.uk   T: 01756 791534
f @beanlovedskipton 🐦 @beanloved 📷 @beanloved

MAP №102 BLOOMFIELD SQUARE

28-30 Gay Lane, Otley, Leeds, West Yorkshire, LS21 1BR

Good coffee and design are happy bedfellows, so Bloomfield Square's combo of speciality beans and letterpress-printing workshop isn't as eclectic as it might at first seem.

Visual creativity comes through in everything here, from the duck-egg blue exterior paintwork to the bare-stone-walled interior decorated with (you guessed it) hand-printed artwork from the back-room studio.

North Star provides the house beans, backed up by Echelon (among other guest roasteries) which stumps up the single origin served every Sunday to give regulars the chance to try something different.

INSIDER'S *tip* ADDITIONAL EVENING EVENTS INCLUDE LIVE MUSIC, FILMS AND TALKS

The friendliest of welcomes is a big part of Bloomfield Square's appeal, so dog walkers and cyclists often detour to drop in. Once through the door they're faced with an agonising choice as the counter groans with tempting cakes under glass domes. Go trad with a generously proportioned scone or tuck in to one of the many vegan treats on offer.

ESTABLISHED
2016

KEY ROASTER
North Star
Coffee Roasters

BREWING METHOD
Espresso, V60

MACHINE
La Marzocco
Linea PB

GRINDER
Mahlkonig K30
ES, Mazzer Luigi

OPENING HOURS
Tue-Thu 9am-4pm
Fri-Sat 9am-5pm
Sun 10am-4pm

---

www.bloomfieldsquare.co.uk   T: 01943 463683

f @bloomfieldsquare   🐦 @bloomfieldsqr   📷 @bloomfield_square

MAP 103 TAMBOURINE COFFEE

38 Bingley Road, Saltaire, West Yorkshire, BD18 4RU

The folk at Tambourine take their neighbourhood coffee shop role pretty seriously, so whether you're meeting friends, catching up on emails or have a toddler in tow, you'll be welcome.

The team have adapted the contemporary space for its kaleidoscope of customers and new parents will find plenty of space for prams while laptop warriors won't need to spar for a plug socket.

INSIDER'S TIP LOOK OUT FOR EXHIBITIONS AND EVENTS FEATURING LOCAL ARTISTS AND DESIGNERS

Quality espresso and artisan bakes are the morning go-to, or hang around to brunch on scrummy dishes like sweetcorn fritters. Lunch is based around crowd-pleasing toasties, bhaji burgers and waffles. And the array of cakes, brownies and Northern Bloc ice creams will delight, whatever the time of day.

The community hub employs North Star for espresso and filter duties, while a rotation of Origin, Girls Who Grind, Maude and Dark Woods provide expert alt options.

ESTABLISHED
2017

KEY ROASTER
North Star
Coffee Roasters

BREWING METHOD
Espresso,
Moccamaster

MACHINE
La Marzocco
Linea

GRINDER
Mahlkonig K30,
Mahlkonig
EK43 S

OPENING HOURS
Mon-Fri 7.30am-5pm
Sat 8.30am-5pm
Sun 9am-4pm

Gluten FREE

BEANS AVAILABLE / INSTORE

WIFI

CYCLE FRIENDLY

OUTDOOR seating

DISABLED ACCESS

BRING YOUR OWN cup.

DOG FRIENDLY

---

www.tambourinecoffee.co.uk   T: 01274 945870

@tambourinecoffe   @tambourinecoffee

MAP № 104 KING COFFEE CO

788 Leeds Road, Bradford, West Yorkshire, BD3 9TY

The slick team behind King Coffee Co have introduced Bradford to a taste of Asian coffee culture.

Inspired to offer an alternative to the city's ever-increasing chains, the team launched this Leeds Road cafe in 2018. The quality coffee proved such a hit that people now travel across the city to sample the different serves.

INSIDER'S TIP DON'T FORGET YOUR LOYALTY CARD – YOUR SEVENTH COFFEE IS ON KING

Colourful compilations such as Kashmiri pink, matcha and chai lattes offer a unique alternative to the bill of espresso based brews. The baristas are super friendly and the vibe welcoming, so pair a Vietnamese cinnamon bun with a petal-dusted Kashmiri latte, and chill out under the neon 'coffee' sign.

On hot days in the city, a tempting chunk of the drinks menu can be blended into iced and frappe versions. Grab a seat outside, order an iced cappuccino and handmade cheesecake and enjoy a regal moment.

ESTABLISHED
2018

KEY ROASTER
Dark Woods Coffee

BREWING METHOD
Espresso, filter

MACHINE
La Spaziale S40 Suprema

GRINDER
Anfim Super Caimano Scody II

OPENING HOURS
Mon-Fri 7.30am-8pm
Sat-Sun 9am-9pm

T: 07704 935509
@kingcoffeeco

MAP № 105 JAVA JOE

1 Corban Street, Bradford, West Yorkshire, BD4 8RH

Dominated by chains pushing commodity grade beans, drive-thrus don't have a great reputation for quality caffeine. However, this Bradford indie is rewriting the rules – one cup of lightly roasted speciality at a time.

The family-run drive-thru (the UK's first speciality pit stop of its kind) serves two different espressos as well as batch brew, so your usual grab-and-go set-up it certainly ain't.

When founder Ryan Gallagher launched Java Joe in 2016, he enrolled the team at Maude in Leeds to roast a house and guest coffee for his Nuova Simonelli machine.

INSIDER'S TIP: THE SALTED CARAMEL BROWNIE IS ADDICTIVELY DELICIOUS

Java's rosetta-adorned flatties and mugs of batch brew don't have to be consumed in the car either. There's plenty of space to sip inside the orange-hued cafe, or perch on one of the few alfresco seats to refuel with an iced latte and something tasty from the seasonal menu.

If 'drive-thru' screams throwaway consumer culture, ditch the preconception: Ryan has introduced a range of reusable cups so visitors can sip on the move with a clean conscience.

ESTABLISHED
2016

KEY ROASTER
Maude
Coffee Roasters

BREWING METHOD
Espresso,
batch brew filter

MACHINE
Nuova Simonelli
Aurelia I

GRINDER
Mythos One

OPENING HOURS
Mon-Fri 6am-8pm
Sat 7am-6pm
Sun 8am-6pm

 Gluten FREE

 BEANS AVAILABLE INSTORE

 WIFI

 CYCLE FRIENDLY

 OUTDOOR SEATING

 DISABLED ACCESS

 BRING YOUR OWN CUP

 DOG FRIENDLY

www.javajoe.co.uk   T: 07944 526053
 @javajoebfd   @javajoetweets   @javajoebradford

MAP No 106 FIKA NORTH

94 Otley Road, Far Headingley, Leeds, West Yorkshire, LS6 4BA

It's the small and thoughtful touches – hand-picked playlists, the texture of the ceramic cups, gold lettering on the windows and ornate tiled floor creeping up the bar – that set this Leeds coffee shop apart from the crowd.

'Swedish vibes with Yorkshire spirit' is how Gemma and Elis Williams describe their new Otley Road venue, and the small-batch roasted coffee, impressive pastries and pleasingly pared-back design fit the fika brief nicely.

Yorkshire is well represented, with the regional roasting contingent enjoying prime place in the hoppers: Maude, Echelon, Casa Espresso and other indies take turns on the trio of grinders.

INSIDER'S TIP SWING BY LATE ON THE WEEKENDS FOR CRAFT BEER, ORGANIC WINE AND COCKTAILS

Neighbouring producers stock the cake counter and provide the ingredients for a menu of homemade food (look out for seasonal specials), while local artists showcase their work on the original stone walls.

For an authentic Scandi brunch, try the skagen: a classic Swedish dish of prawns in crème fraîche with dill, served on toasted sourdough.

ESTABLISHED
2019

KEY ROASTER
Multiple roasters

BREWING METHOD
Espresso, batch brew

MACHINE
La Marzocco Linea PB ABR

GRINDER
Fiorenzato F64 EVO x 2, Wilfa

OPENING HOURS
Mon-Fri 8am-6pm
Sat-Sun 9am-6pm

www.fikanorth.co.uk   T: 07742 450716

f @fikanorth   @fikanorth

MAP№ 107 BOWERY CAFE

54 Otley Road, Leeds, West Yorkshire, LS6 2AL

Be prepared to be bowled over by a visit to Bowery in the cricketing mecca that is Headingley.

The faint roar of a match crowd can often be heard drifting on the breeze from the cricket ground to Bowery's end-of-terrace location, where big windows invite punters in to browse crafts, absorb art and kick back with a coffee.

Like the test match teams that regularly visit the Emerald Headingley Stadium, the house coffee has an antipodean pedigree and New Zealand Allpress beans are prepared as espresso, pourover and cold brew.

On the food front, hearty lunch plates are heaped with freshly chopped salads, while cakes are created in-house with the clear intention of leading you astray. Oreo brownie, anyone? Thought so ...

INSIDER'S tip JOIN HEAD BARISTA GED TOGHER'S WORKSHOPS TO LEARN HOW TO BREW LIKE A PRO

If you can drag yourself away from the buzzy atmos of the cafe, take time to peruse some contemporary artwork or check out the timetable of craft events.

ESTABLISHED
2008

KEY ROASTER
Allpress Espresso

BREWING METHOD
Espresso, pourover, cold brew

MACHINE
La Marzocco Linea Classic

GRINDER
Mazzer Major Electronic

OPENING HOURS
Mon-Thu
8.30am-6.30pm
Fri-Sat 8.30am-6pm
Sun 10am-5pm

www.thebowery.org   T: 01132 242284
f @boweryleeds   🐦 @theboweryarts   📷 @boweryleeds

MAP№ 108 DOT THE LIONS

Leeds Arts University, Blenheim Walk, Leeds, West Yorkshire, LS2 9AQ

The staff and students of Leeds Arts University couldn't believe their luck when Laynes Espresso revealed that the uni foyer would be the location of its much-anticipated second outpost.

Dave Olejnik's central coffee shop has been a pillar of the city's speciality scene since opening in 2011, and this sister venue upholds its stonking reputation for quality brews and wholesome food – just in a take-out-only format.

INSIDER'S TIP GRAB A BREKKIE OF CHIA PUDDING WITH MANGO, COCONUT AND RASPBERRIES

From Monday to Friday, artsy folk can fuel their creativity with carefully poured Dark Woods espresso, Echelon batch brew and freshly prepped salads, sandwiches and bakes. The team craft everything from scratch in the tiny kitchen and have taken the area's lunchtime offering to a whole new level.

It's not only undergrads and lecturers who've made the bright and bold venue (designed by former students) their new go-to. The local workforce has also been getting in on the action with pre-work flatties, stuffed-vine-leaf lunches and afternoon-slump smoothies.

ESTABLISHED
2019

KEY ROASTER
Dark Woods Coffee

BREWING METHOD
Espresso, batch brew

MACHINE
Synesso S200

GRINDER
Victoria Arduino Mythos One

OPENING HOURS
Mon-Fri 8.30am-4pm

Gluten FREE

BEANS AVAILABLE
INSTORE

WIFI

CYCLE FRIENDLY

DISABLED ACCESS

BRING YOUR OWN Cup

T: 07447 944444

f @dotthelions   🐦 @dotthelions   📷 @dotthelions

ⁿ⁰.109 ARCHIVE

94 Kirkstall Road, Leeds, West Yorkshire, LS3 1HD

If you're up for a bit of celeb spotting as you savour your batch brew, schedule an early appearance at this coffee house attached to Prime Studios.

Once ITV's video archive, the space has been reinvented as a contemporary coffee shop and is now a favourite haunt of the actors who spend their days filming next door.

A line-up of indie roasters and a slick Synesso MVP Hydra machine provide a coffee experience of star quality: Glasgow roastery start-up Blak Nektar is currently headlining, with support from local roasters Maude and Echelon on pourover and batch brew.

INSIDER'S tip LIKE WHAT YOU'RE DRINKING? PICK UP A BAG FROM THE RETAIL SELECTION

It's not just the coffee that's building Archive its fanbase, as delicious brunches of oozing croque monsieur and vegan pancakes have also garnered fans from Leeds' foodie fraternity. Visit at lunchtime for light and fluffy potato gnocchi cooked in garlic and chive cream.

The sleek coffee house (all geometric prints, dark wood and yellow accents) is attached to a huge events space and licenced bar which is available to hire.

ESTABLISHED
2019

KEY ROASTER
Blak Nektar
Speciality Coffee

BREWING METHOD
Espresso,
batch brew,
pourover

MACHINE
Synesso MVP
Hydra

GRINDER
Compak F10,
Slingshot C688

OPENING HOURS
Mon-Thu 8am-4pm
Fri 8am-6pm
Sat 9am-6pm
Sun 9am-4pm

Gluten FREE · BEANS AVAILABLE INSTORE · WIFI · CYCLE FRIENDLY · OUTDOOR seating · DISABLED ACCESS · DOG FRIENDLY

www.archiveleeds.co.uk   T: 07444 710139
f @archiveleeds   🐦 @archiveleeds   📷 @archiveleeds

MAP №110 KAPOW COFFEE

15 Thornton's Arcade, Leeds, West Yorkshire, LS1 6LQ

As you wander through majestic Thornton's Arcade, with its towering glass ceiling and decorative ironwork, expect to find yourself inexorably drawn in to Kapow by the tempting waft of freshly pulled espresso.

INSIDER'S TIP AFTER-HOURS EVENTS INCLUDE CUPPING SESSIONS AND CRAFT WORKSHOPS

Kapow is – quite rightly – a coffee shop that puts a spotlight on, well, coffee. With so many exciting varieties to explore, expect to discover a new bean on the block every couple of weeks. Rounton, Fortitude and Neighbourhood are among the varied and numerous roasters that have featured.

Alongside guest espressos, daily-changing batch brews and house blends from Union also feature. If you want to double up on the treat, chase your pick with a fruity muffin or gooey brownie.

The cafe inhabits a character-packed building set over three skinny storeys, and sunshine-orange walls make a cheerfully modern splash against the Arcade's ostentatious Victorian architecture.

ESTABLISHED
2013

KEY ROASTER
Union Hand-
Roasted Coffee

BREWING METHOD
Espresso, V60,
batch filter

MACHINE
Kees van
der Westen

GRINDER
Dalla Corte

OPENING HOURS
Mon-Sat 8am-6pm
Sun 10am-5pm

www.kapowcoffee.co.uk

f @kapowthorntons 🐦 @kapowcoffee 📷 @kapowcoffee

MAP 111 LA BOTTEGA MILANESE – BOND COURT

2 Bond Court, Leeds, West Yorkshire, LS1 2JZ

Forget long and lazy brunches or spending hours poring over a single filter coffee; Milanese cafe culture centres around quality food and caffeine in a fast-paced environment. It's this authentic Italian experience that Alex Galantino has recreated in Bond Court for the busy people of Leeds.

The tempo is lively, the service slick and the coffee of the highest standard. Alex teamed up with Huddersfield's Dark Woods to create the bespoke blend for his two coffee shops (find the other at The Headrow) which you can sample as espresso, V60, AeroPress or batch filter.

INSIDER'S tip TOAST LA BOTTEGA'S 10TH YEAR IN BUSINESS WITH ONE OF THE SIGNATURE ITALIAN PASTRIES

If you're planning on sticking around for lunch (try the focaccia stuffed with fresh ingredients) grab one of the stools that line the concrete bar running the length of the shop. That said, you'll need to arrive before the midday rush to claim one. Stakes for the alfresco seats are even higher on sunny days in the city, or there's the option of making like an Italian and simply sinking a quick espresso at the counter.

ESTABLISHED
2009

KEY ROASTER
Dark Woods Coffee

BREWING METHOD
Espresso, V60, batch filter, AeroPress

MACHINE
La Marzocco Linea PB

GRINDER
Anfim Pratica, Cimbali Magnum

OPENING HOURS
Mon-Fri 7am-6pm
Sat 9am-6pm
Sun 10am-5pm

www.labottegamilanese.co.uk   T: 01132 431102

f @labottega.milanese   🐦 @bottegamilanese   📷 @labottegamilanese

MAP № 112 THE BREW SOCIETY

26 Aire Street, Leeds, West Yorkshire, LS1 4HT

Customers who care about the quality of coffee they pick up on their way to work are usually also fussy about the calibre of beer they down after a long day in the office. So curating speciality beans and craft beers under one roof was a no-brainer for Brew Society founders Nino, Rich and Danni.

By day, their sociable space specialises in single origin espresso roasted in the city by North Star. Batch brew and V60 pourovers are also available for those looking to road-test the latest indie rocking the guest spot.

Come late afternoon, revellers swap flat whites for micro-brewery ales and beers. A rotating line-up on cask and keg showcases local brews from the likes of Turning Point, Verdant and Harrogate Brewery.

INSIDER'S TIP CHECK OUT SISTER SHOP NO35 HARROGATE FOR FURTHER CAFFEINATED THRILLS

When the weather's playing ball, the alfresco seating area is *the* place in which to savour a morning espresso or evening G&T; spot the planters where the team are growing hops for future brewing projects.

ESTABLISHED
2019

KEY ROASTER
North Star
Coffee Roasters

BREWING METHOD
Espresso, V60,
batch brew

MACHINE
La Marzocco
Linea Classic

GRINDER
Anfim, Mazzer
Super Jolly

OPENING HOURS
Mon-Wed 7am-10pm
Thu-Fri 7am-11pm
Sat 12pm-11pm

www.brewsociety.co.uk
f @thebrewsocietyleeds @thebrewsocietyleeds

MAP№ 113 LAYNES ESPRESSO

14–16 New Station Street, Leeds, West Yorkshire, LS1 5DL

It's easy for perma-busy cafes to become complacent, but keeping the food and coffee current, creative and exciting takes energy. It's something the team at Laynes know all about: they haven't taken their foot off the gas since launching as a speciality pioneer in 2011.

An extension in 2017 allowed founder Dave Olejnik to expand the brunch offering and also make more room for locals and the visitors who pour out of Leeds Station and into Laynes for speciality grade caffeine.

INSIDER'S tip CHECK OUT NEW SISTER VENUE, DOT THE LIONS, AT LEEDS ARTS UNI

The coffee offering is kept fresh and funky via a roster of European roasters on batch brew and V60, while beans for espresso are usually sourced from Square Mile – although the team switch it up if they stumble upon an especially delicious find.

If you're staying to eat, check out the specials board before committing to any of the contemporary classics. Recent seasonal dishes include rarebit with garlic mushrooms, and french toast with lemon and vanilla.

ESTABLISHED
2011

KEY ROASTER
Square Mile
Coffee Roasters

BREWING METHOD
Espresso, V60,
batch brew

MACHINE
Synesso MVP

GRINDER
Victoria Arduino
Mythos One

OPENING HOURS
Mon-Fri **7**am-**6**pm
Sat-Sun **8**am-**5**pm

Gluten FREE

BEANS AVAILABLE INSTORE

WIFI

BRING YOUR OWN Cup.

DOG FRIENDLY

www.laynesespresso.co.uk   T: 07828 823189

f @laynesespresso   🐦 @laynesespresso   📷 @laynesespresso

MAP№ 114 OUT OF THE WOODS – GRANARY WHARF

Watermans Place, Granary Wharf, Leeds, West Yorkshire, LS1 4GL

Short of taking off to the sparkling fjords, there are few places where you can drink coffee surrounded by such woodland-esque waterside cosiness. With its log-cabin feel, this little sister coffee shop to the Water Lane stalwart is the perfect place to sip a Dark Woods espresso and indulge in an afternoon of tranquil canal-gazing.

Enjoy the view through floor-to-ceiling windows or grab a seat outside when the weather's clear – cosy blankets and squidgy pillows allow year-round alfresco sipping. Come Saturday morning, the canal-side seats fill with brunchers getting their fix of the new weekend menu.

INSIDER'S TIP SEE HOW MANY SQUIRRELS YOU CAN SPOT SCAMPERING AROUND THE CAFE

Cyclists and dog walkers exploring the Leeds and Liverpool Canal come here to fuel up on fresh sarnies, soups and salads. Commuters bustling to and from Leeds Station, meanwhile, brighten their working day with the prospect of homemade bakes and guest beans from the likes of Girls Who Grind, North Star and Echelon.

ESTABLISHED
2010

KEY ROASTER
Dark Woods Coffee

BREWING METHOD
Espresso, batch brew, V60, cold brew

MACHINE
La Spaziale

GRINDER
Mahlkonig K30

OPENING HOURS
Mon-Fri 7am-4pm
Sat-Sun 9am-3pm

www.outofthewoods.me.uk   T: 01132 454144
f @outofthewoodsuk   @outofthewoodsuk   @outofthewoodsuk

MAP № 115 OUT OF THE WOODS – WATER LANE

113 Water Lane, Leeds, West Yorkshire, LS11 5WD

After a spot of retail therapy in Leeds, it's good to have a cosy cafe (outside the bustle of the city centre) up your sleeve where you can revive with a decent cup of coffee. Shopping fatigue is soon remedied at this relaxed and friendly coffee shop, tucked away in the indie hub of Holbeck Urban Village.

INSIDER'S TIP STEEP YOURSELF IN A BIT OF HISTORY WITH A VISIT TO NEARBY TEMPLE WORKS

Fortify yourself with a chunky sarnie: regulars extol the virtues of the Yorkshire roast ham with cheese, wholegrain mustard, tomato chutney and spinach. There's also a menu of hearty lunches including spicy veg pakora and Swedish meatballs, all crafted from the best local ingredients.

Brownies, blondies and the buttery salted caramel millionaire's shortbread pair well with roasts from Yorkshire chums Dark Woods. Adventurous bean buffs will also want to explore the rotating roster of guests from the likes of Unorthodox, Echelon, North Star and Girls Who Grind.

ESTABLISHED
2006

KEY ROASTER
Dark Woods Coffee

BREWING METHOD
Espresso, batch brew, cold brew

MACHINE
La Marzocco Linea PB

GRINDER
Mahlkonig K30

OPENING HOURS
Mon-Fri **7**am-**4**pm

 Gluten FREE

 BEANS AVAILABLE INSTORE

 WIFI

 OUTDOOR seating

 DISABLED ACCESS

 BRING YOUR OWN cup.

 DOG FRIENDLY

---

www.outofthewoods.me.uk   T: 01132 448123

f @outofthewoodsuk   🐦 @outofthewoodsuk   📷 @outofthewoodsuk

№ 116 COFFEEVOLUTION

8 Church Street, Huddersfield, West Yorkshire, HD1 1DD

Coffeevolution is to Huddersfield coffee culture what *Cheers* was to the Boston bar scene, and folk have been visiting to sip and socialise at the award winning coffee house for 20 years.

The camaraderie between staff and customers is cracking and, if you're a local, it's odds on they'll even know your name.

Baristas enjoy introducing newbies and regulars alike to the world of alternative brewing methods and speciality bean finds, and they're always happy to talk through the flavour profile of each option.

INSIDER'S tip ASK AT THE COUNTER FOR SPECIAL DOGGY TREATS FOR YOUR POOCH

A profusion of serve styles, including cold brew and a house coffee stout, means that even jaded coffee lovers will find something to invigorate their palates.

The beans are roasted less than a mile away at sister roastery Bean Brothers, while guests from the likes of Berlin's The Barn offer yet more titillation.

Bag a seat on a bench by the floor-to-ceiling window and watch the world go by as you sink your teeth into a scrumptious bacon and cream cheese bagel or a homebaked vegan muffin.

ESTABLISHED
2000

KEY ROASTER
Bean Brothers
Coffee Company

BREWING METHOD
Espresso,
V60, Chemex,
AeroPress,
syphon,
cold brew

MACHINE
La Marzocco
FB80

GRINDER
Mahlkonig K30
Twin, Mahlkonig
EK43

OPENING HOURS
Mon-Fri **7**am-**7**pm
Sat **7.30**am-**7**pm
Sun **9**am-**6**pm

Gluten FREE

BEANS AVAILABLE
IN STORE

WIFI

CYCLE FRIENDLY

OUTDOOR seating

DISABLED ACCESS

BRING YOUR OWN cup

COFFEE COURSES

DOG FRIENDLY

---

www.coffeevolution.co.uk T: 01484 432881

f @coffeevolution 🐦 @coffeevolution 📷 @coffeevolutionhuddersfield

MAP №117 ARCADE COFFEE & FOOD

9-10 Byram Arcade, Huddersfield, West Yorkshire, HD1 1ND

This coffee shop in Huddersfield's gothic Byram Arcade has built an enviable reputation for top-notch brews and killer brunches since it opened in 2017.

The beans putting Arcade on the coffee map are sourced from local indie Darks Woods, which roasts the house espresso six miles away in a tranquil spot next to the River Colne. Guest roasts from the likes of Maude, Girls Who Grind, Craft House, Five Elephant and North Star are also available if you fancy exploring further afield.

INSIDER'S TIP GRAB A SEAT IN THE NEW STUDY SPACE, THEN FUEL UP WITH COFFEE AND CAKE

While the weekday food offering is particularly drool-worthy (go full English or check out daily specials such as jackfruit tacos), Sunday lunch is the real speciality. Tables get booked up quickly, so you'll need to be on it if you want in on the beef brisket, Yorkshire pud, roasties and seasonal veg action.

Plant-based visitors aren't left out either and Arcade's katsu tofu burger has led many a just-popping-in-for-a-coffee customer astray. Craft beers, wines and Bloody Marys round out a weekend visit in style.

ESTABLISHED
2017

KEY ROASTER
Dark Woods
Coffee

BREWING METHOD
Espresso,
batch filter

MACHINE
La Marzocco
Linea Classic

GRINDER
Cimbali Magnum,
Mahlkonig EK43

OPENING HOURS
Mon-Fri 8am-6pm
Sat 9am-6pm
Sun 10am-4pm

 Gluten FREE

 BEANS AVAILABLE INSTORE

 WIFI

 OUTDOOR seating

 DISABLED ACCESS

 BRING YOUR OWN CUP

 DOG FRIENDLY

T: 01484 511148

 f @arcadecoffeefood 🐦 @arcade_coffee 📷 @rcadecoffeefood

№ 118 WIRED COFFEE AND CAKE

17 Church Street, Honley, Holmfirth, West Yorkshire, HD9 6AH

Wired started life as a bespoke wedding cake business, but began introducing its beautiful bakes to the masses in December 2018 when founder Oliver Schofield branched out and opened a cafe in a former bookmakers.

He had become hooked on the speciality stuff while delivering cakes to venues across Yorkshire, so knew that only top-notch coffee would do Wired's sweet masterpieces justice.

INSIDER'S TIP GET STUCK IN TO A WIRED PLATTER OF LOCAL GOODIES SUCH AS PORK PIES AND CHEESES

Oliver spent two years researching the best local suppliers before opening and eventually plumped for Huddersfield's Dark Woods for the house roast. Find its Arboretum Espresso alongside seasonal single origins from a roster of guests in the Mahlkonig and Macap grinders.

The team also dabble in light breakfasts, savoury lunches and Brew Tea Co blends but, let's face it, who's going to turn down a wedge of peanut butter brownie and a silky flat white?

ESTABLISHED
2018

KEY ROASTER
Dark Woods Coffee

BREWING METHOD
Espresso, batch filter, Clever Dripper, AeroPress

MACHINE
Iberital Expression Pro

GRINDER
Mahlkonig K30, Macap

OPENING HOURS
Fri **9**am-**4**pm
Sat **9.30**am-**4**pm
Sun **10**am-**3**pm

 Gluten FREE
 BEANS AVAILABLE INSTORE
 WIFI
 CYCLE FRIENDLY
 OUTDOOR SEATING
 BRING YOUR OWN CUP

T: 07598 931448
f @wiredcoffeeandcake 🐦 @wiredcoffeeand1 📷 @wiredcoffeeandcake

№119 BLOC

19a Huddersfield Road, Holmfirth, West Yorkshire, HD9 2JR

After years playing catch-up with poached eggs and pancakes, toast is finally enjoying a resurgence thanks to the sourdough movement which catapulted it back into the foodie spotlight.

Meg Beever's sunshiney Holmfirth cafe is a celebration of the staple and her concept menu of 'things on toast' is an ode to the king of carbs. Artisan bread comes from a bakery just a few miles away, where dough is proved for a minimum of 18 hours to guarantee a gorgeously chewy crust.

INSIDER'S TIP CATCH BRIGHT YELLOW LAND ROVER 'ROAD BLOC' AT EVENTS ACROSS YORKSHIRE

Bloc purists top their toast with preserves or smashed avo, while trendsetters seek inspiration from the specials menu where combos such as salami, spinach and spicy guac change by the week. If there's room after your any-time-of-day brunch sesh, round out a visit with a hunk of brownie or scoop of vegan ice cream.

Coffee fuelling the party is sourced from Dark Woods and can be sampled as espresso, V60 or batch filter. And, if the sun's shining, head to the (dog-friendly) decking to sip alfresco.

ESTABLISHED
2016

KEY ROASTER
Dark Woods
Coffee

BREWING METHOD
Espresso,
V60, batch filter

MACHINE
La Marzocco
Linea Classic

GRINDER
Cimbali Magnum

OPENING HOURS
Mon-Sun 9am-4pm

www.bloctoast.co.uk   T: 01484 687228

f @blocholmfirth   🐦 @bloc_toast   📷 @bloc_toast

ROASTERS

PROBAT

York Coffee Emporium №121

120

6 Talbot Yard, Yorkersgate, Malton, North Yorkshire, YO17 7FT

This family-run roastery not only has one of the most eco-friendly and energy efficient roasters at its heart, it's also stepped up its planet-friendly practices.

David and Ruth Elkington (aided and abetted by mini apprentices Erin, Betsy and goldendoodle Skye) are on a mission to reduce the amount of packaging associated with their business. Many bean-buying customers now take along their own containers, while wholesalers are supplied with sealed, reusable buckets in lieu of foil-lined paper bags.

2015

Diedrich IR-12
12kg

ONSITE

Sound ethics are just one of the many good reasons to swing by the Malton roastery which is housed among a cluster of artisan food and drink businesses in the 18th century stable yard of Grade II-listed Talbot Hotel.

Be prepared to be dazzled by the huge selection of house-roasted single origins which can be sampled at the purpose-built bar as espresso or pourover. Those in the know arrive armed with empties so they can stock up on their favourites to brew at home.

www.roostcoffee.co.uk   01653 697635

@roostcoffeeandroastery   @roost_coffee   @roost_coffee

121

Unit 4-5, Rose Centre, York Business Park, York, North Yorkshire, YO26 6RX

With two Q graders on roasting duties and a whopping 47-strong bill of blends and single origins, this Yorkshire roastery proves that quality needn't be sacrificed when you're dealing in quantity.

Roasters Laurence and Richard are constantly on the trail of new and exciting beans and, when they're not behind the vintage Probat, are to be found sampling fresh lots from ethical importers who support programmes such as International Women's Coffee Alliance and Girls Gotta Run. The duo's recent finds have been so popular with local cafes and businesses that they've just installed a chunky new 20kg Sivetz to keep up with demand.

2012

Vintage Probat 25kg

Sivetz 20kg

Otto Swadlo 5kg

Solar 2kg

THE ETHICAL IMPORTERS SUPPORT PROGRAMMES SUCH AS INTERNATIONAL WOMEN'S COFFEE ALLIANCE

The Emporium's subscription service allows bean geeks to tour the coffee-growing belt from the comfort of their kitchens: current customer faves include Clifford (citrus, toffee and milk choc flavours) and the plum and dark chocolate notes of Whip-Ma-Whop-Ma Espresso – named after the smallest street in York.

www.yorkcoffeeemporium.co.uk   01904 799399

@yorkemporiumcoffee   @york_emporium   @york_emporium

122 ECHELON COFFEE ROASTERS

Unit 20, Penraevon Industrial Estate, Penraevon Street, Leeds, West Yorkshire, LS7 2AW

Ben Craggs admits that before he met his wife Monika (who was managing a Leeds cafe at the time) he didn't know what great coffee was.

His gradual transformation from a newbie into a fully blown coffee nerd took place while working at the British Embassy in Belgium. Inspired by Ghent cafe culture and his neighbour (former Belgian AeroPress champion) Charlene DeBuysere, Ben started using his downtime to experiment with roasting on a 1kg Probat.

On their return to the UK, Ben and Monika upgraded to a 6kg Giesen and set up Echelon. The name? It's a reference to the diagonal line that Tour de France riders form during a crosswind and a nod to Ben's other great passion: cycling.

THE OPTION OF BUYING COFFEE BEANS BY WEIGHT REDUCES PLASTIC USE

The pair are on a mission to ensure the farmers' dedication to growing an exceptional product is expressed in every cup, so they use only ethical importers who can guarantee the traceability of each crop. This year, they're also moving to fully recyclable packaging, with the option of buying beans by weight to reduce waste.

ESTABLISHED
2018

ROASTER
MAKE & SIZE
Giesen W6A 6kg

www.echeloncoffee.co.uk   07889 247264

@echeloncoffee   @echelonroasters   @echeloncoffee

123

Unit 5, Briar Rhydding, Otley Road, Shipley, West Yorkshire, BD17 7JW

There's never a quiet moment at this Bradford micro-roastery thanks to the 11 espresso blends and single origins on the go at any one time. Consequently, head roaster Jonnie is almost always found at his trusty Probat, tending the next batch of beans.

The passion for coffee has deep roots at Casa Espresso: 20 years ago, the father of founder Nino even travelled across the Italian countryside on a hunt for the world's best espresso machine, bringing home a Sanremo.

If you're new to Casa's seasonal coffees, the Charlestown Espresso's smooth dark chocolate notes are a cracking place to start. Looking for something a little funkier? Check out the seasonal selection of single origins or the Great Taste award winning Unione blend.

Always keen to improve sustainability, the Casa crew give coffee chaff from the roasting process to local farmers to use as chicken bedding, and package beans in fully recyclable carbon-neutral bags. They also support the World Coffee Research Checkoff programme.

2015

Probat 5kg

www.casaespresso.co.uk   01274 595841

@casaespresso   @casa_espresso   @casa_espresso

124 DARK WOODS COFFEE

Holme Mills, West Slaithwaite Road, Marsden, Huddersfield, West Yorkshire, HD7 6LS

Dark Woods won more Great Taste awards in 2018 and 2019 than any other coffee company (it's the only roastery ever to win a top Golden Fork gong twice) – and it only takes a sniff around the rural west Yorkshire roastery to understand why.

This highly experienced team of coffee pros are on a mission to explore and unlock flavour possibilities. They experiment relentlessly, tickling out vibrancy and revealing depths of flavour in a wide range of speciality grade beans which they roast in an array of styles to suit palates of all persuasions.

'THIS HIGHLY EXPERIENCED TEAM OF COFFEE PROS ARE ON A MISSION TO EXPLORE AND UNLOCK FLAVOUR'

Even the most hardcore of coffee connoisseurs will find beans to surprise and delight. Dark Woods creates bespoke roasts for the exacting customers of Michelin starred restaurant L'Enclume in the Lake District, as well as Fortnum & Mason and Liberty.

Check the website for regular events; the monthly pop-up cafe attracts hundreds of coffee fans to the renovated riverside mill.

ESTABLISHED
2013

ROASTER
MAKE & SIZE
Vintage Probat
UG22
Probatone 5kg

OPEN
(BY APPOINTMENT)

COFFEE
COURSES

COURSES

BEANS
AVAILABLE

www.darkwoodscoffee.co.uk   01484 843141

@darkwoodscoffee   @darkwoodscoffee   @darkwoodscoffee

125

Bewley's, Bent Ley Road, Meltham, Holmfirth, West Yorkshire, HD9 4EP

Grumpy Mule aims to make customers smile with its irreverent, tongue-in-cheek brand – its unusual name referencing the days when mules were used to haul coffee cherries down the mountains.

Fun it may be, but quiet it certainly isn't and the roastery, which is nestled in the undulating hills of the Holme Valley, seemingly never sleeps. Two huge gas-fired Probat drum roasters and a 35kg Loring Smart are the tools of the roasters' trade and turn out winning coffee in volume. In fact, the company has bagged 38 Great Taste awards since 2014 – gaining gongs for both its roasted-to-order batch coffee and retail range.

The roastery – which also runs SCA-accredited courses – lives by the following ethos: traceable, ethical, sustainable and arabica.

The team focus on Fairtrade, direct trade and also work with organic farmers and growers, with the aim of ensuring that everyone benefits from Grumpy Mule's participation in the coffee cycle.

ESTABLISHED
2006

ROASTER MAKE & SIZE
Probat G120 120kg
Probat G60 60kg
Loring Kestrel 35kg

www.grumpymule.co.uk   01484 855500
@grumpymulecoffee   @grumpymule   @grumpy_mule

№126 ARTEMIS COLD BREW COFFEE

Womersley, North Yorkshire, DN6 9BB

Crafting quality cold brew before it went mainstream, Artemis founder Ben Barker has ethically sourced and then slowly extracted single origin beans to create lip-smackingly delicious caffeine since 2015.

ESTABLISHED
2015

COLD BREW +NITRO AVAILABLE

ONLINE

'THE CONCENTRATE AND NITRO USE JUST TWO CORE INGREDIENTS: WATER AND SPECIALITY GRADE COFFEE BEANS'

In the four years that have passed, Ben has expanded the team and the retail selection to become one of the major players in the cold brew market. Nitro, cold brew concentrate and nitro Espresso Martini products have all joined the Artemis family and furthered its quest for exciting flavour profiles and texture potential.

Just like the original cold brew, the concentrate and nitro use just two core ingredients: water and speciality grade coffee beans. *'It's about focusing on one thing and doing it well,'* explains Ben. *'We work closely with our roasters to ensure all of our coffee is sustainably sourced and roasted to produce a bright, clean and fruity chilled coffee with a balanced acidity.'*

Pick up Artemis' products at stockists across the UK (including at festivals) or from the website.

---

www.artemisbrew.co.uk　T: 01977 621691

f @artemisbrew　🐦 @artemisbrew　📷 @artemisbrew

SOUTH &
EAST
YORKSHIRE

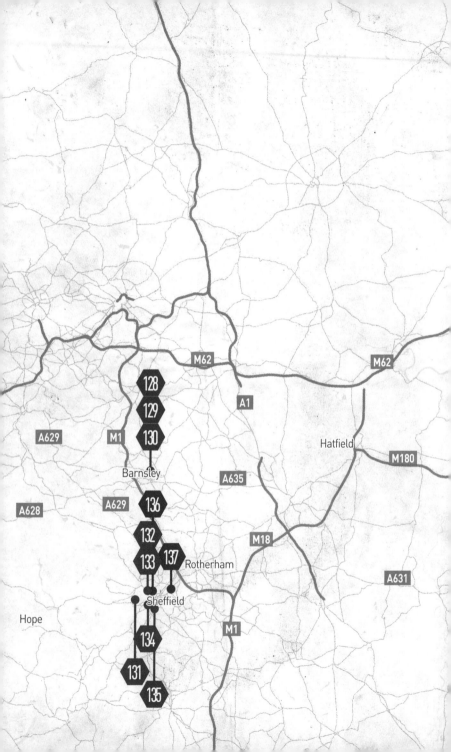

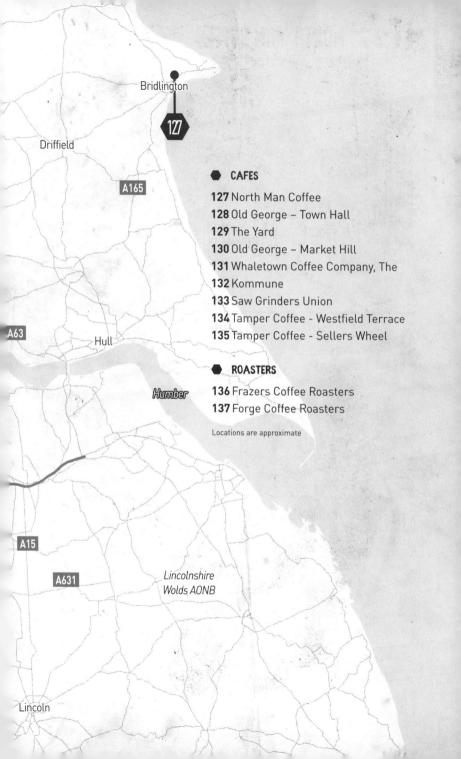

Bridlington

127

Driffield

A165

A63

Hull

Humber

A15

A631

Lincolnshire
Wolds AONB

Lincoln

● **CAFES**

127 North Man Coffee
128 Old George – Town Hall
129 The Yard
130 Old George – Market Hill
131 Whaletown Coffee Company, The
132 Kommune
133 Saw Grinders Union
134 Tamper Coffee - Westfield Terrace
135 Tamper Coffee - Sellers Wheel

● **ROASTERS**

136 Frazers Coffee Roasters
137 Forge Coffee Roasters

Locations are approximate

MAP№ 127 NORTH MAN COFFEE

7 Manor Street, Bridlington, East Yorkshire, YO15 2SA

Refreshing Bridlington's food and drink scene – one carefully crafted dish and expertly pulled espresso at a time – is the mission at North Man Coffee.

Boldly eschewing the seaside town's chippie culture, the dedicated team deal in veggie-focused fodder and speciality-standard brews. From bread to relish (and pretty much everything in between), almost every item on the menu is made in-house.

Sift your way through a list of classic brunch dishes and specials, being sure to leave room for one of the sweet masterpieces that crown the counter.

INSIDER'S TIP LOOK OUT FOR NORTH MAN AFTER-HOURS FOODIE EVENTS

London's Square Mile heads up the single origin coffee offering, with support from guests such as Workshop, Round Hill and Casa Espresso.

The minimalist decor focuses the senses on what's in your cup, as well as making a pretty sweet backdrop if you're planning on taking a few snaps of your brew. If it's sunny, head outdoors and feast alfresco on the likes of shakshuka, focaccia and grilled salads.

ESTABLISHED
2016

KEY ROASTER
Square Mile
Coffee Roasters

BREWING METHOD
Espresso, drip

MACHINE
Synesso Hydra

GRINDER
Mythos One
Clima Pro

OPENING HOURS
Mon-Sat **8**am-**5**pm
Sun **10**am-**3**pm

T: 01262 673530

f @northmancoffee @northmancoffee

MAP№ 128 OLD GEORGE – TOWN HALL

Town Hall, Church Street, Barnsley, South Yorkshire, S70 2TA

Within the grand surroundings of Barnsley Town Hall, you'll find this little brother to the original Old George coffee house on nearby Market Hill.

The setting is pretty special: bright and airy with booths for cosy chats, as well as some high spots in which to perch for people watching.

Whether you're grabbing and going or pulling up a pew, you'll be treated to drinks that have been meticulously prepared with beans fresh from Sheffield's Forge Coffee Roasters.

INSIDER'S TIP HIRE THE IMPRESSIVE SPACE AS A VENUE FOR YOUR OWN EVENT

There's always a Fetco batch brew to be had, as well as the usual espresso based faves on which the baristas showcase their impressive latte art skills.

'Things on toast' is how the team describe the menu, but it's a bit of an understatement. The sandwiches come stuffed with unctuous fillings, while grilled croque monsieur and rarebit ooze with stringy cheese and delicious accompaniments.

ESTABLISHED
2019

KEY ROASTER
Forge Coffee Roasters

BREWING METHOD
Espresso, batch brew

MACHINE
La Marzocco Linea PB

GRINDER
Mahlkonig E65 S, Mahlkonig EK43 S

OPENING HOURS
Mon-Fri 9am-4pm

www.old-george.co.uk   T: 01226 217129

f @oldgeorgetownhall   🐦 @oldgeorgebarn   📷 @oldgeorgetownhall

MAP№ 129 THE YARD

The Civic, Hanson Street, Barnsley, South Yorkshire, S70 2HZ

As the third member of the burgeoning Old George crew, The Yard has snapped up a rather splendid space within The Civic. The cultural hub is where theatre, dance and all sorts of arty events take place, so including top-notch coffee feels absolutely spot on.

The Yard lures in creative types and coffee lovers with the brightest, pinkest custom La Marzocco Strada around. It earns its keep too, enabling the baristas to craft exquisite espresso using fairly traded and super fresh beans which have whizzed up the M1 from Sheffield's Forge Coffee Roasters. If you prefer a more low-tech approach, AeroPress is also available.

INSIDER'S tip SWING BY FOR AN AMERICANO COCKTAIL OF VERMOUTH AND BITTER CAMPARI

While it's worth popping in just for a brew, if you've time to linger don't miss out on the eats. Start your day with shakshuka (baked eggs, tomatoey harissa beans and sourdough toast) or lunch on one of the outrageously good sharing boards. PM visits demand afternoon tea, while on Sundays The Yard offers its hearty take on the traditional roast.

ESTABLISHED
2019

KEY ROASTER
Forge Coffee
Roasters

BREWING METHOD
Espresso,
AeroPress

MACHINE
La Marzocco
Strada AV

GRINDER
Mahlkonig E65 S,
Mahlkonig EK43 S

OPENING HOURS
Sun-Thu 9am-4pm
Fri-Sat 9am-9pm

Gluten FREE

BEANS AVAILABLE
INSTORE

WIFI

OUTDOOR Seating

DISABLED ACCESS

BRING YOUR OWN Cup

---

www.old-george.co.uk   T: 01226 695700

f @theyardbarnsley   🐦 @oldgeorgebarn   📷 @theyardbarnsley

MAP № 130 OLD GEORGE – MARKET HILL

14 Market Hill, Barnsley, South Yorkshire, S70 2QE

The team at Old George are on a mission to serve exceptional coffee to the people of Barnsley, choosing a Grade II-listed building bang in the middle of town as their assignment HQ.

Speciality grade beans are carefully sourced from Forge Coffee Roasters in nearby Sheffield, before finishing their journey to caffeine nirvana on Old George's La Marzocco KB90. The ergonomic machine saves baristas from wrist strain and turns out an epic espresso too. Fans of filter prep can plump for AeroPress or V60 options.

INSIDER'S TIP WORKER BEES WILL LIKE OLD GEORGE'S QUICK-AS LUNCHES

Alongside the caffeine offering, the cafe's refreshing juices – pressed in-house – are popular, while the food is homemade and creatively indulgent.

Breakfasts are set-you-up-for-the-day hearty while zingy salads bring crunch to lunchtime. Come mid-afternoon, the chunky slabs of cake and traybake and piled-high afternoon teas are the obvious go-to.

ESTABLISHED
2017

KEY ROASTER
Forge Coffee
Roasters

BREWING METHOD
Espresso, V60,
AeroPress

MACHINE
La Marzocco
KB90

GRINDER
Mahlkonig E65 S,
Mahlkonig EK43 S

OPENING HOURS
Mon-Sun 9am-4pm

Gluten FREE

BEANS AVAILABLE INSTORE

WIFI

OUTDOOR SEATING

DISABLED & ACCESS

BRING YOUR OWN CUP

DOG FRIENDLY

---

www.old-george.co.uk   T: 01226 217169

f @oldgeorgebarn   🐦 @oldgeorgebarn   📷 @oldgeorgebarnsley

Northern Distributor of Victoria Arduino espresso machines and grinders.

MAP 131 THE WHALETOWN COFFEE COMPANY

227 Crookes, Sheffield, South Yorkshire, S10 1TE

There's a reassuring simplicity to the pared-back interior design at The Whaletown Coffee Company. Reassuring because, with nothing to distract from the coffee, you know they're serious about crafting a mean cup.

Expect nothing but single origins here, from both hero roaster Outpost and a swathe of European guests that changes monthly. Mok (Belgium), Drop (Sweden) and Five Elephant (Germany) have all featured.

INSIDER'S TIP TRY A FLAT RED – A SINGLE ORIGIN ROOIBOS TEA RUN THROUGH THE LA MARZOCCO

Brewing is a precise affair – these are beans worth taking time over after all – with every shot weighed and complex flavours expertly tickled out. Go for straight-up espresso from the La Marzocco, add the delights of steamed milk or take the V60, Chemex or batch brew routes.

The innovation that drives the coffee offering is echoed in the food and drink menus. Smørrebrød – open sandwiches on Danish rye – and creatively flavoured macarons offer alt cafe options, while offbeat drinks like the Orca (a quadruple-shot latte) and the Jacques Cousteau (hot choc and Bombay-spiced chai) surprise and delight.

ESTABLISHED
2018

KEY ROASTER
Outpost Coffee Roasters

BREWING METHOD
Espresso, V60, Chemex, batch brew, cold brew

MACHINE
La Marzocco Linea Classic

GRINDER
Mazzer

OPENING HOURS
Mon-Fri 8.30am-5pm
Sat 9am-5pm
Sun 10am-4pm

 Gluten FREE
 BEANS AVAILABLE INSTORE
 WIFI
 OUTDOOR SEATING
 DISABLED ACCESS
 BRING YOUR OWN CUP
 COFFEE COURSES

DOG FRIENDLY

T: 07872 602232
f @whaletowncoffeeco @whaletowncoffee @whaletowncoffeeco

MAP №132 KOMMUNE

Castle House, Angel Street, Sheffield, South Yorkshire, S3 8DA

After brewing some of the best speciality coffee and serving stonking brunch and breakfast dishes in the city for over half a decade, the Tamper crew have decided to let their foodie chums in on the act.

The result is Kommune, Sheffield's exciting new food hall concept. It gathers a range of indie food stalls (pick from South American, Korean and Yorkshire inspired eats among other delights) which sit alongside Tamper's coffee and baked goods offering in the former Co-op at Castle House.

The vibe is industrial urban so it's a must-visit for snap-happy brunchers. Sip beautifully crafted Ozone coffee as espresso (or choose between the two Hasbean batch brews) while you weigh up the edible options.

INSIDER'S TIP FINESSE YOUR LATTE ART SKILLS AT ONE OF THE KOMMUNE COFFEE EVENTS

A mammoth range of baked goods (made by Tamper's sister team at The Depot Bakery) vie to be paired with your house or guest roast. Stumped? Pay homage to Tamper's NZ roots with a hokey-pokey-flavoured Sweet As ice cream.

ESTABLISHED
2019

KEY ROASTER
Ozone Coffee Roasters

BREWING METHOD
Espresso, batch brew, V60, cold brew

MACHINE
La Marzocco Strada EP

GRINDER
Mythos One, Mahlkonig EK43, Mahlkonig Peak

OPENING HOURS
Thu-Fri 8am-9pm
Sat 9am-9pm
Sun 9am-6pm

www.thedepotbakery.co.uk T: 01142 757779
f @thedepotbakery @thedepotbakery @thedepotbakery

MAP №133 SAW GRINDERS UNION

Globe Works, Penistone Road, Sheffield, South Yorkshire, S6 3AE

This fresh venue charmingly fuses Sheffield's long-held rep for carefully crafted silverware with its more recent one for top-notch coffee.

The team behind Saw Grinders have retained the old cutlery factory's industrial vibe, creating a relaxed cafe/bar area with patched-up and pared-back walls. This spills onto a courtyard that's lush with tumbling greenery and, by night, you could be in one of New York's hipper neighbourhoods.

INSIDER'S TIP KEEP 'EM PEELED FOR HAND BREW – COMING SOON

Espresso based drinks make good use of beans from Extract, while a guest spot on batch brew is filled by a different roaster each month (recent residencies include Maude and Round Hill).

The coffee's great but the food takes equal billing. Bacon-topped potato cakes make a hearty brunch, while the fondue is fabulous to share with friends. Vegan and veggie options slip seamlessly into the mix and you'll also find the current dish-du-jour of poutine – cheesy fries slathered in gravy – on the menu.

ESTABLISHED
2019

KEY ROASTER
Extract Coffee Roasters

BREWING METHOD
Espresso, batch brew

MACHINE
La Marzocco KB90

GRINDER
Mythos One

OPENING HOURS
Mon-Sun 8am-5pm

Gluten FREE

BEANS AVAILABLE INSTORE

WIFI

CYCLE FRIENDLY

OUTDOOR seating

DISABLED ACCESS

BRING YOUR OWN cup.

DOG FRIENDLY

www.sawgrindersunion.com   T: 01142 010065

f @sawgrindersunion   @saw.grinders.union

MAP № 134 TAMPER – WESTFIELD TERRACE

9 Westfield Terrace, Sheffield, South Yorkshire, S1 4GH

This Tamper outpost may not deal in the same abundance of brunch and breakfast choices as its big sister venues, but for a beautiful coffee experience in the heart of the city it's hard to beat.

Break up an afternoon of indie shopping around Division Street with a syrupy espresso and slab of something fabulous at this tiny hidden haunt.

Knowledgeable baristas are always happy to share their thoughts on the day's pick of the beans. Alongside the Ozone house blend you'll find a regularly changing selection of seasonal single origins. Guest roaster Hasbean features lots from Ethiopia, Costa Rica, Ecuador, Kenya and beyond.

INSIDER'S tip TRY NEW COFFEES AT THE MONTHLY PUBLIC CUPPING SESSIONS

Pair your brew with a delicate macaron or a sourdough toastie – all the goods are handcrafted by the Tamper team at The Depot Bakery at Kelham Island.

ESTABLISHED
2011

KEY ROASTER
Multiple roasters

BREWING METHOD
Espresso,
Kalita Wave,
Chemex,
AeroPress

MACHINE
La Marzocco
Strada EP

GRINDER
Mahlkonig EK43,
Mythos One
Clima Pro

OPENING HOURS
Mon-Fri 8am-4pm
Sat 9am-4pm
Sun 10am-4pm

Gluten FREE

BEANS AVAILABLE
INSTORE

WIFI

CYCLE FRIENDLY

OUTDOOR seating

DISABLED ACCESS

BRING YOUR OWN cup

COFFEE COURSES

DOG FRIENDLY

www.tampercoffee.co.uk   T: 01143 271080
f @tampercoffee   🐦 @tampercoffee   📷 @tampercoffeewt

№135 TAMPER – SELLERS WHEEL

149 Arundel Street, Sheffield, South Yorkshire, S1 2NU

This much-loved urban coffee shop has paid homage to its owner Jon Perry's New Zealand roots since it popped up in Sheffield's Cultural Industries Quarter six years ago.

Locals stream in at all hours of the day for breakfast and brunch dishes which are crafted with creative aplomb. Old favourites like eggs benny and avo on toast rub shoulders with the likes of montreal benedict (poached eggs, bubble and squeak, smoked salmon and hollandaise on crusty bloomer, FYI).

INSIDE'S tip HIRE THE GRADE II-LISTED VENUE FOR AN INDUSTRIAL-CHIC SOIRÉE

Sure, the food's great, but it's coffee that's kept the Tamper trio of cafes at the top of the game for so long.

Beans from Kiwi roaster Ozone provide the go-to house blend, while there is always a pick'n'mix of interesting guests sourced from around the world if you're feeling promiscuous. Go classic espresso or plump for methods such as Kalita drip to sample the selection of single origins from Hasbean.

ESTABLISHED
2013

KEY ROASTER
Multiple roasters

BREWING METHOD
Espresso, Kalita Wave, batch brew, AeroPress, cold brew

MACHINE
La Marzocco Linea PB

GRINDER
Mythos One, Mahlkonig EK43

OPENING HOURS
Mon-Thu 8am-5pm
Fri-Sat 8am-6pm
Sun 9am-4pm

Gluten FREE

BEANS AVAILABLE INSTORE

WIFI

CYCLE FRIENDLY

OUTDOOR seating

DISABLED ACCESS

BRING YOUR OWN cup

COFFEE COURSES

DOG FRIENDLY

---

www.tampercoffee.co.uk   T: 01142 757970

f @tampercoffee   🐦 @tampercoffee   📷 @tampercoffeesw

ROASTERS

136 FRAZER'S COFFEE ROASTERS

46-47 Wilson Street, Neepsend, Sheffield, South Yorkshire, S3 8DD

Starting from scratch is no mean feat for a small batch roaster – and it's even tougher if you decide to first build the machine on which you'll be bronzing the beans.

It's this no-corners-cut approach that Frazer Habershon took when he launched his Neepsend roastery in 2014. After discovering an old cast iron roasting drum, Frazer utilised what was being produced on his doorstep and built the rest of the machine from local steel. The result of his hard work is an impressive piece of kit on which he cooks up consistently good coffee.

ESTABLISHED
2014

ROASTER
MAKE & SIZE
Handmade 12kg

OPEN
TO THE PUBLIC

COFFEE
COURSES

BEANS
AVAILABLE

"LIKE A SNICKERS BAR IN A BOTTLE"

Collaborating with people who are equally passionate about their craft is important to Frazer and the team. They work with quality-driven coffee farmers as well as offering coffee shops specialist training to ensure the final cup hits the highest standards.

A new facility has allowed the guys to expand into the production of cold brew. Made with single origin Peruvian beans which have been extracted in cold water for 18-24 hours, the rich and nutty result tastes like a Snickers bar in a bottle.

www.frazerscoffeeroasters.co.uk   01142 015815

@frazerscoffeeroasters   @frazerscoffee   @frazerscoffeeroasters

№132
Kommune

137 FORGE COFFEE ROASTERS

Don Road, Sheffield, South Yorkshire, S9 2TF

Based in Sheffield's former industrial heartland, Forge Coffee Roasters takes inspiration from the quality craftsmanship and creativity on which the city's reputation was built. The beans are even cooked up in a building where a traditional forge once operated.

The brand's well-established blends like Invicta, Ruskin, Kropp and Trinity are "forged" on a traditional Giesen roaster and can, along with seasonal single origins, be sourced online and from the roastery.

The crew offer an honest and independent consultancy service and also find time to resell and service La Marzocco and Conti espresso machines.

"QUALITY CRAFTSMANSHIP AND CREATIVITY ON WHICH THE CITY'S REPUTATION WAS BUILT"

In addition, the roasters take their coffee to events via a caffeinated fleet: the 1935 Bedford truck and 1933 Austin 7 van have recently been joined by a 1938 Oldsmobile flatbed truck and a 1939 Triumph sidecar with a mounted La Marzocco GS3.

ESTABLISHED
2015

ROASTER
MAKE & SIZE
Giesen W30A
30kg
Giesen W15A
15kg

www.forgecoffeeroasters.co.uk   01142 441361

@forgeroasters   @forgeroasters   @forgeroasters

LINCOLNSHIRE, NOTTINGHAMSHIRE & DERBYSHIRE

№143
Elements Tea and
Coffee House

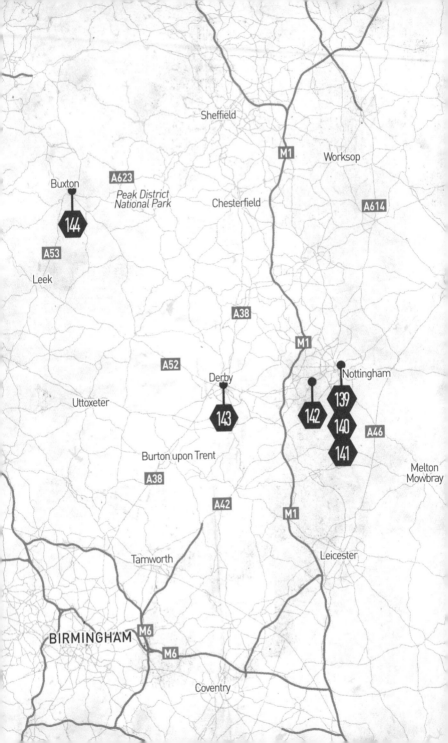

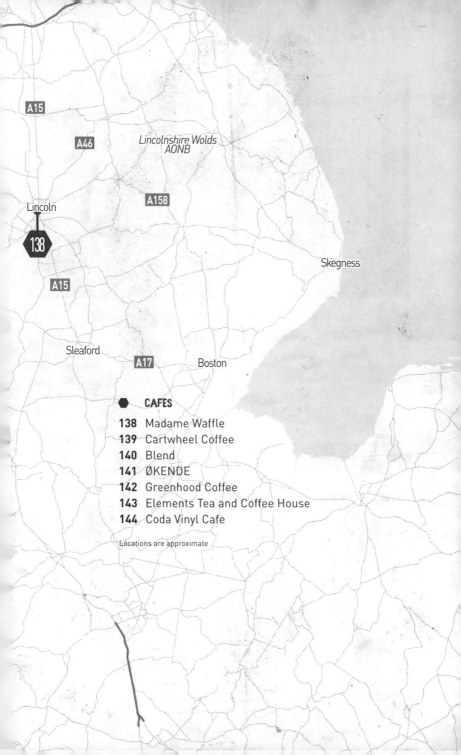

A15

A46

*Lincolnshire Wolds
AONB*

A158

Lincoln

138

A15

Skegness

Sleaford

A17

Boston

Locations are approximate

MAP№ 138 MADAME WAFFLE

285 High Street, Lincoln, Lincolnshire, LN2 1AL

Speciality fans with a penchant for freshly griddled waffles usually can't believe their luck when they stumble upon Lincoln's batter and bean emporium.

For over four years, Madame founders Sharon and Bruce Whetton have kept the waffle irons sizzling and the La Marzocco firing on all cylinders, ready to fuel their customers with gravity-defying stacks of bronzed batter and expertly poured flat whites.

INSIDER'S *tip* CHECK OUT THE NEW CO-WORKING SPACE IN THE BASEMENT

Accredited SCA trainer Bruce takes care of the coffee, while Sharon is responsible for the tempting bill of breakfast and lunch plates. This combination of quality coffee and sweet 'n' savoury thrills saw the cafe scoop a Good Food Award in 2019.

Three distinctly designed floors – plus an outside seating area – provide plenty of space in which to experience the Madame Waffle magic. Square Mile keeps the hopper humming with top-quality beans, while Bruce's crack team of baristas have the skills to make them shine. Plump for the house-fave Red Brick blend and bliss out on orange, fudge, cherry and vanilla notes.

ESTABLISHED
2015

KEY ROASTER
Square Mile
Coffee Roasters

BREWING METHOD
Espresso,
Chemex, V60,
AeroPress

MACHINE
La Marzocco
Linea PB

GRINDER
Mythos One x 2,
Mahlkonig EK43

OPENING HOURS
Mon-Sat 9am-5pm
Sun 10am-4pm

---

www.madamewaffle.co.uk   **T:** 01522 512286

f @madamewaffleuk   🐦 @madamewaffleuk   📷 @madamewaffle

MAP№ 139 CARTWHEEL COFFEE

16 Low Pavement, Nottingham, Nottinghamshire, NG1 7DL

Veer off the main shopping drag onto Low Pavement to find Nottingham's speciality fans spilling out into the cobbled lane from this popular coffee shop.

Named after owners Alex and Becci's acrobatic escapades down the street some years previously, Cartwheel Coffee sprung onto the indie scene in 2016 and has been perma-busy ever since.

Alex's coffee experience spans two decades and, with a SWAT team of Q graders, he roasts seasonally rotating beans for the cafe's Black Eagle machine and armoury of filter gear. His enthusiasm for making quality coffee accessible to all is infectious and the skilled baristas host cuppings and offer tasting flights for those who want to broaden their palates.

INSIDER'S TIP SECURE A SPOT AT THE FINE DINING POP-UP WHICH TAKES PLACE EVERY OTHER MONTH

Two experienced chefs ensure that the food equals the coffee standards and craft a seasonal menu of locally sourced and plant-based options. Brunch is especially good and most who visit fall head-over-heels for the chorizo pan hash.

ESTABLISHED
2016

KEY ROASTER
Cartwheel Coffee

BREWING METHOD
Espresso, Kalita Wave, syphon

MACHINE
Victoria Arduino Black Eagle Gravimetric

GRINDER
Mahlkonig EK43, Mythos One

OPENING HOURS
Mon-Fri **8.30**am-**5**pm
Sat **9**am-**5.30**pm
Sun **10**am-**4**pm

Gluten FREE

BEANS AVAILABLE INSTORE

WIFI

CYCLE FRIENDLY

OUTDOOR SEATING

DISABLED ACCESS

BRING YOUR OWN Cup

COFFEE COURSES

DOG FRIENDLY

---

www.cartwheelcoffee.com   T: 01159 598434

f @cartwheelcoffee   🐦 @carthweelcoffee   📷 @carthweelcoffee

ᴹᴬᴾ꜀ 140 BLEND

Unit 30, Avenue C Sneinton Market, Nottingham, Nottinghamshire, NG1 1DW

The grilled-cheese and flattie gods behind Blend have added a distinctive notch to Nottingham's burgeoning coffee belt.

Since launching the cafe in Sneinton Market in 2017, the laid-back team have built a rep for their killer toasties and locally roasted coffee. And with Stewarts of Trent Bridge bronzing the greens for the brew bar from their roastery just next door, expect the coffee to be as lip-smackingly fresh as the sourdough.

INSIDE'S TIP PLANNING A BIG EVENT? DECENT COFFEE IS A MUST. BOOK BLEND'S RETRO COFFEE TRAILER 'HELGA'

The cafe's location among a throng of indie retailers in the bustling market lures creative types and passing shoppers seeking caffeinated solace away from the city centre. Those with time to kill head to the window bench which lines the roomy venue to linger over a batch brew. In summer, the plaza terrace is the spot to soak up artsy vibes with a cold brew.

A menu of between-bread cheesiness is split into two sections: herbivores and carnivores, so both meat-eaters and veggies can bliss out on the carby goods. Channel Queen B vibes with a Brieyonce or let loose with a Kevin Baconator.

ESTABLISHED
2017

KEY ROASTER
Stewarts of Trent Bridge

BREWING METHOD
Espresso, V60, batch brew, nitro

MACHINE
Conti Monte Carlo

GRINDER
Compak E83

OPENING HOURS
Mon-Thu 7am-6pm
Fri 7am-8pm
Sat-Sun 9am-6pm

---

www.blendnottingham.co.uk   T: 01158 389350

f @blendnottingham   🐦 @blendnottingham   📷 @blendnottingham

MAP № 141 ØKENDE

22 Gordon Road, West Bridgford, Nottingham, Nottinghamshire, NG2 5LN

Photo: Angus Sung

While custom and top-end espresso machines can be an enticing focal point of a cafe's interior, there's no denying that, due to their chunky size, they form a barrier between barista and customer.

It's one of the reasons why Josh Rowe and Annie Stanford installed a Mavam (an espresso machine that has nearly all its mechanisms hidden under the counter) at their West Bridgford venue. The two group heads that sprout from the jet-black bar also happen to blend seamlessly with the shop's ultra-minimalist white and bleached-wood interior.

INSIDER'S TIP THE VIBE MAY BE MINIMALIST, BUT FEEL FREE TO BRING ALONG YOUR POOCH

Connecting with customers and chatting coffee is super important to Josh and Annie. Their line-up of roasters spans Europe and beyond, often featuring indie roasteries rarely seen in Nottinghamshire, and the open-plan cafe layout encourages conversation about what's in the cup.

A small, refined brunch menu showcasing local and seasonal ingredients is in keeping with the pared-back vibe.

ESTABLISHED
2018

KEY ROASTER
La Cabra Coffee Roasters

BREWING METHOD
Espresso, V60

MACHINE
Mavam

GRINDER
Mythos One, Mahlkonig EK43

OPENING HOURS
Mon-Sat
7.30am-**5.30**pm
Sun **9**am-**4**pm

Gluten FREE

BEANS AVAILABLE INSTORE

WIFI

CYCLE FRIENDLY

OUTDOOR SEATING

DISABLED ACCESS

BRING YOUR OWN CUP

DOG FRIENDLY

---

www.okende.com
 f @okendecoffee 🐦 @okendecoffee 📷 @okendecoffee

Organic ACORN DAIRY

FOR BARISTAS
BY ORGANIC COWS

- PERFECT FOR GREAT LATTE ART
- COMPLEMENTS COFFEE FLAVOURS
- BATCH TESTED FOR CONSISTENCY
- OPTIMISED FAT AND PROTEIN RATIO
- SILKY SMOOTH, LONG-LASTING MICRO FOAM
- MADE WITH AWARD-WINNING ORGANIC MILK

Contact Acorn Dairy for your local distributor

acorndairy.co.uk
01325 466999

SOIL ASSOCIATION ORGANIC

THE FOOD AWARDS ENGLAND 2017 WINNER

GOOD DAIRY AWARD

142 GREENHOOD COFFEE

38 High Road, Beeston, Nottingham, Nottinghamshire, NG9 2JP

With floor-to-ceiling windows, bright white walls and minimalist design, this light and airy coffee shop is the kind of place you want to stick around and order another espresso – even if you're already skirting dangerously close to your caffeine threshold.

After outgrowing his role at a big coffee chain then dabbling in the indie scene, founder and barista Rory Archer launched Greenhood in a roomy corner spot in Beeston in 2015.

The two-storey coffee house quickly became a hub for the community, and inside you'll find tat-stamped students sipping V60s alongside old-timers sampling the latest Colonna beans via AeroPress. Rory's super-inclusive approach to coffee and the chilled vibe make everyone feel at home here.

INSIDER'S TIP: RORY IS A BIT OF A LOCAL CELEB FOR HIS MILK STEAMING SKILLS

European roasters such as Three Marks, Five Elephant and April feature regularly and there are usually two espressos and two filters to choose from. For sustenance, hit up the counter stocked with cakes and pastries or check out the bill of freshly stacked bagels.

ESTABLISHED
2015

KEY ROASTER
Colonna Coffee

BREWING METHOD
Espresso, V60, AeroPress

MACHINE
Kees van der Westen Spirit

GRINDER
Mythos One x 2, Mahlkonig EK43

OPENING HOURS
Mon-Fri 7am-5pm
Sat 8am-5pm

BEANS AVAILABLE INSTORE

WIFI

DISABLED ACCESS

BRING YOUR OWN Cup

f @greenhoodcoffee 🐦 @greenhoodcoffee 📷 @greenhoodcoffee

MAP№ 143 ELEMENTS TEA AND COFFEE HOUSE

6 Royal Buildings, Victoria Street, Derby, Derbyshire, DE1 1ES

A great coffee experience is only ever as good as the sum of its parts – and thankfully this city centre hangout has all the elements required of a top-notch speciality stop.

Stratford-upon-Avon's Monsoon Estates provides the raw materials for the syrupy espresso pulled through the La Marzocco machine, while a series of guest roasters (including Hundred House, Melbourne in Lichfield and Colonna) guarantee additional choices for filter, espresso or decaf.

Tea receives similarly specialist attention and loose-leaves are sourced from a number of artisan blenders – choose from 20-plus infusions.

INSIDER'S tip BOOK ON TO ONE OF THE REGULAR HOME BREW WORKSHOPS

A lengthy list of local suppliers and a confident kitchen team mean the menu of casual eats also hits the mark. Swing by on a Sunday to brunch on turmeric porridge, eggs benedict and stacked sausage sarnies, or visit anytime to chow down on the house waffles.

Keep a check on social media to find out about up-coming fine dining evening events.

ESTABLISHED
2018

KEY ROASTER
Monsoon Estates

BREWING METHOD
Espresso, V60, AeroPress, cold brew

MACHINE
La Marzocco Linea PB

GRINDER
Anfim Pratica x 2, Mazzer Mini

OPENING HOURS
Mon-Thu **9.30**am-**5**pm
Fri **9.30**am-**11**pm
Sat **8.30**am-**11**pm
Sun **10**am-**4**pm

---

www.elementsderby.co.uk   T: 01332 349591

f @elementsteaandcoffeederby   🐦 @elementsderby   📷 @elementsteaandcoffeehouse

№144 CODA VINYL CAFE

2 South Avenue, Buxton, Derbyshire, SK17 6JZ

Opening a cafe can be a unique opportunity to combine an interest in speciality coffee with other passions, and for Barbara Morse and Neil McDonald that meant being able to brew locally roasted beans while expanding their vinyl collection.

A great soundtrack is an often-forgotten yet oh-so-important ingredient for a memorable coffee experience, and at Coda espresso based drinks are accompanied by classic anthems and eclectic tunes. The resulting vibe is buzzy and friendly – visitors are even encouraged to browse the collection and choose the next track.

INSIDER'S TIP ARRIVE EARLY IF YOU WANT TO GET FIRST DIBS ON THE COSY LEATHER SOFA

Beans destined for the Sanremo grinder make the short trip across town from Buxton Roastery and are best sampled with an accompanying wedge of cake. Homemade masterpieces change daily but you'll always find crowd-pleasers like carrot cake, toffee and chocolate, and lemon and blueberry.

There are also breakfast and lunch options if you're after something more substantial. Sandwich specials include smoked mackerel with horseradish and pickled radish, as well as brisket with beer onions and blue cheese.

ESTABLISHED
2018

KEY ROASTER
Buxton Roastery

BREWING METHOD
Espresso

MACHINE
Sanremo Zoe

GRINDER
Sanremo SR50

OPENING HOURS
Tue-Fri 10am-4pm
Sat 9am-4pm
Sun 11am-4pm

Gluten FREE

BEANS AVAILABLE INSTORE

WIFI

OUTDOOR seating

DOG FRIENDLY

T: 01298 938228

f @codavinylcafe 🐦 @codavinylcafe @ @codavinylcafe

STAFFORDSHIRE,
WEST MIDLANDS
WARWICKSHIRE
& LEICESTERSHIRE

The Early Bird № 153

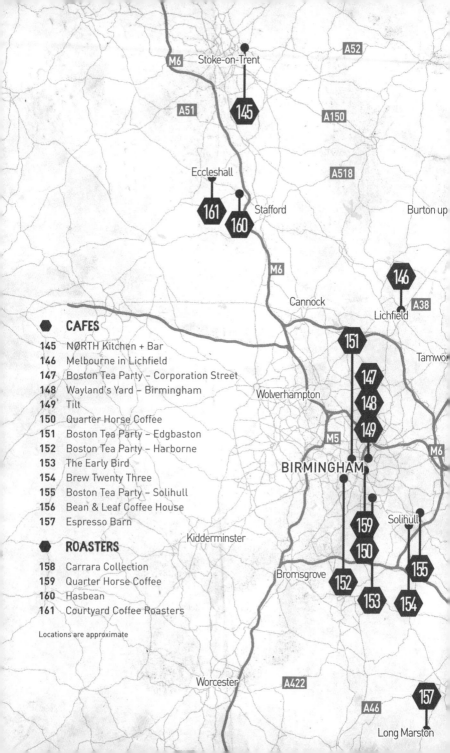

● CAFES

145 NØRTH Kitchen + Bar
146 Melbourne in Lichfield
147 Boston Tea Party – Corporation Street
148 Wayland's Yard – Birmingham
149 Tilt
150 Quarter Horse Coffee
151 Boston Tea Party – Edgbaston
152 Boston Tea Party – Harborne
153 The Early Bird
154 Brew Twenty Three
155 Boston Tea Party – Solihull
156 Bean & Leaf Coffee House
157 Espresso Barn

● ROASTERS

158 Carrara Collection
159 Quarter Horse Coffee
160 Hasbean
161 Courtyard Coffee Roasters

Locations are approximate

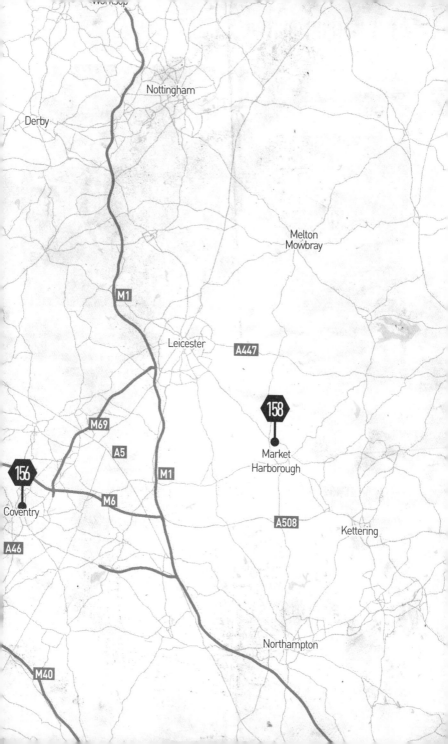

MAP №145 NØRTH KITCHEN + BAR

31 Piccadilly, Hanley, Stoke-on-Trent, Staffordshire, ST1 1EN

In recognition of the popularity of Nordic coffee culture, in 2019 the owners of this Hanley venue pared back the interiors and introduced a Scandi menu.

Food has always been a big draw at the popular spot and, in line with the new northern vibe, the chefs have refined the bill to fit a healthy-but-still-comforting brief. The fresh line-up namedrops more superfoods than a wellness blogger and includes a good show of veggie and vegan options, so you won't be short on hitting your five a day.

INSIDER'S TIP — HEAD OVER AT THE END OF THE WEEK FOR SUNDAY-ONLY BRUNCH DISHES

To kickstart a productive morning, try a bulletproof espresso made with grass-fed-cow's milk butter, coconut oil, vanilla and maple syrup. Those opting for a more conventional cup are well served by the Climpson & Sons house blend or single origin guest.

As the day winds down, detox juices and nourishing smoothies give way to a less virtuous drinks bill including the house Espresso Martini and a selection of craft beers.

ESTABLISHED
2015

KEY ROASTER
Climpson & Sons

BREWING METHOD
Espresso, V60,
AeroPress, filter

MACHINE
La Marzocco
Linea PB

GRINDER
Mythos One x 2

OPENING HOURS
Mon-Tue 10am-5pm
Wed-Thu 10am-8pm
Fri-Sat 10am-10pm
Sun 11am-4pm

BEANS AVAILABLE INSTORE

WIFI

CYCLE FRIENDLY

OUTDOOR SEATING

DISABLED ACCESS

BRING YOUR OWN CUP

DOG FRIENDLY

www.northcq.co.uk   T: 01782 871299
f @northcq

^{MAP №}146 MELBOURNE IN LICHFIELD

32-34 Bird Street, Lichfield, Staffordshire, WS13 6PR

I t's not difficult to suss out the inspiration behind this lively Lichfield coffee shop. With its graffiti-art walls, super chilled vibe and flat whites a-go-go, Melbourne is clearly a hit of Aussie caffeine culture in Staffordshire.

'As with the city it's named after, Melbourne is unashamedly itself,' says founder Deborah Pease.

Those craving the sights and smells of Melbs will revel in the friendly welcome, sunshine yellow theme (which extends from the Conti Monte Carlo machine to the cups and bathroom door) and the waft of freshly bronzed beans from the – also canary coloured – roaster at the front of the shop.

The house single origin joins a Rwandan roast from Union and a roster of guest coffees from indies such as Clifton, Nude and Ngopi. The team love to keep the drinks menu fresh so alongside seasonal coffees you'll find turmeric lattes, turkish delight hot choc and energising chai.

^{INSIDER'S} *tip* LOOK OUT FOR SPEAKEASY EVENTS, POP-UP YOGA SESSIONS AND RETRO GAMES NIGHTS

An Oz-inspired cafe experience wouldn't be complete without brunch: get your fill from the line-up of porridge bowls, toasties and cruffins.

ESTABLISHED
2017

KEY ROASTER
Multiple
roasters

BREWING METHOD
Espresso, V60,
AeroPress

MACHINE
Conti Monte
Carlo

GRINDER
Sanremo SR70 x 3,
Ditting, Mignon

OPENING HOURS
Mon-Fri **7.30**am-**4**pm
Sat **8**am-**4**pm
Sun **9**am-**2**pm

f @melbourneinlichfield   🐦 @melbsinlich   📷 @melbourneinlichfield

Nº147 BOSTON TEA PARTY – CORPORATION STREET

190 Corporation Street, Birmingham, West Midlands, B4 6QD

Amid the bustle of Birmingham's shopping district, and just a quick coffee-dash from Aston University, this rather grand Boston Tea Party heaves with caffeine lovers who pile in to the funky space to get their daily speciality fix.

With seats for over 120 bottoms, there's lots of room for all of its loyal followers to get comfy – even during the morning rush. Whether you're here to hunker down in one of the booths with a textbook, meet friends for brunch at a large farmhouse table, or grab a coffee-to-go in your KeepCup, squeezing in isn't a problem.

INSIDER'S TIP HAIR OF THE DOG? ADD A SPICY BLOODY MARY TO YOUR BRUNCH ORDER

After the breakfast-time blitz, the pace slows down and the all-day feasting really gets going. Brunch favourites such as the chorizo hash and avocado toast are guaranteed crowd-pleasers, plus there are usually a couple of specials such as spiced lamb flatbread to entice you away from your usual order.

If you're planning on picking up an Extract house espresso for the road you'll need to remember your reusable: BTP went disposable-cup-free in 2018, though you can borrow one if you left yours at home.

ESTABLISHED
2013

KEY ROASTER
Extract Coffee Roasters

BREWING METHOD
Espresso, filter

MACHINE
La Marzocco Linea PB

GRINDER
Mythos One x 2

OPENING HOURS
Mon-Sat 7am-6pm
Sun 9am-5pm

www.bostonteaparty.co.uk T: 01212 178045
f @btpbirmingham 🐦 @btpcafes 📷 @btpbirmingham

148 WAYLAND'S YARD – BIRMINGHAM

42 Bull Street, Birmingham, West Midlands, B4 6AF

Baristas slinging shots in the heart of Birmingham know that keeping the morning rush-hour queue to a minimum is the key to happy customers, but the team behind the brew bar at Wayland's central outpost also appreciate that compromising on quality isn't an option.

Pre-9am, the stylishly distressed space hums with business folk picking up a Method espresso en route to work. When 1pm rolls around, they return for a working lunch of halloumi and mushroom hash or a freshly rolled wrap stuffed with locally sourced ingredients.

INSIDER'S TIP HIRE WAYLAND'S CONVERTED HORSEBOX COFFEE BAR FOR YOUR NEXT EVENT

It's not just worker bees who've made Wayland's deceptively roomy Birmingham outpost their regular haunt, however. A well-equipped brew bar and four-strong coffee line-up has also put the cafe on every local coffee buff's radar, while an epic brunch menu means it's the go-to for families and friends looking for a quality weekend chow down.

Community events keep the space open after hours – find the details on upcoming poetry jams, open mic nights and more on social media.

ESTABLISHED
2018

KEY ROASTER
Method Coffee Roasters

BREWING METHOD
Espresso, V60, AeroPress, cold brew

MACHINE
La Marzocco Linea PB ABR x 2

GRINDER
Mahlkonig K30 Air, Mahlkonig EK43, Mahlkonig Peak

OPENING HOURS
Mon-Fri 7am-6pm
Sat 8am-4pm
Sun 9am-4pm

---

www.waylandsyard.com

 f @waylandsyardbirmingham 🐦 @waylandsyard 📷 @waylandsyard

MAP№ 149 TILT

2 City Arcade, Union Street, Birmingham, West Midlands, B2 4TX

Pinball wizard? You don't have to settle for lukewarm beers in a dark amusement hall as this speciality coffee house and craft beer emporium houses a 20-strong army of the machines.

Fulfilling every teenager's dream, founders Kirk and Richard combined their coffee, beer and pinball fandoms to launch their own 'barcade' in 2015.

Pop culture enthusiasts can dive into three floors of classic arcade games at Tilt, heading to the brew bar between rounds for a next-level coffee experience.

Espresso from Italian outfit Gardelli regularly hits the hopper, though beans change on a weekly basis and often showcase other international roasters such as La Cabra, Drop Coffee and Five Elephant.

INSIDER'S tip THINK YOU'VE GOT WHAT IT TAKES? SIGN UP TO TILT'S MONTHLY PINBALL LEAGUE

Fancy something stronger? Tilt's craft beer line-up roadtrips across the UK, Europe and America – find out what will be appearing next in can and on keg via social. Flagging competitors who need to refuel for the next round can scoff slabs of bundt cake, locally made by Bake.

ESTABLISHED
2015

KEY ROASTER
Gardelli Specialty Coffees

BREWING METHOD
Espresso, Kalita Wave, batch brew

MACHINE
La Marzocco Linea PB ABT

GRINDER
Mythos One x 2, Mahlkonig EK43

OPENING HOURS
Mon-Thu 10am-11pm
Fri-Sat 10am-12am
Sun 10am-10pm

Gluten FREE

BEANS AVAILABLE IN STORE

WIFI

CYCLE FRIENDLY

DISABLED ACCESS

BRING YOUR OWN CUP

DOG FRIENDLY

---

www.tiltbrum.com T: 01216 431048
f @tiltbrum 🐦 @tilt_brum 📷 @tilt_brum

MAP 150 QUARTER HORSE COFFEE

88-90 Bristol Street, Birmingham, West Midlands, B5 7AH

It's a gratifying experience to explore a menu of seasonal coffees and hear the machine in which they were roasted chugging away in the background.

Anyone wanting to find out more about the process can chat to the well-versed baristas who are keen to elaborate on the line-up of beans being pulled through the La Marzocco KB90 (the 31st to be built and one of the first outside of London). And, with the Giesen roaster fired up three times a week and seasonal lots changing every month or so, there's a huge selection to road test.

INSIDER'S TIP: THE CREW HOST MONTHLY ESPRESSO AND HOME BREW MASTERCLASSES

A hefty retail selection offers further experimentation at home; there are usually up to ten single origins and blends available to take away. Amateur brewers can also pick up kit such as V60, AeroPress and filter papers.

Those sticking around blitz their inbox at one of the wooden tables, catch up with chums over flat whites and toasted banana bread, or simply revel in a bit of time out with a cup of coffee in one hand and a good read in the other.

The sunny alfresco space out back is the place to be when Brum is blessed with good weather.

ESTABLISHED
2012

KEY ROASTER
Quarter Horse Coffee

BREWING METHOD
Espresso, Kalita Wave, Marco SP9 filter

MACHINE
La Marzocco KB90, Marco SP9

GRINDER
Nuova Simonelli Mythos One

OPENING HOURS
Mon-Fri 8am-6pm
Sat-Sun 9am-5pm

www.quarterhorsecoffee.com   T: 01214 489660

@qtrhorsecoffee   @quarterhorsecoffee

DEVELOPED WITH BARISTAS FOR BARISTAS
• Perfect for latte art
• No added sugar
• Cholesterol free, low fat alternative to milk
• 30% less calories than skimmed & regular soy milk
UNSWEETENED
BLUE DIAMOND ALMONDS
Almond Breeze
Serving Suggestion
Rich & Creamy
BARISTA BLEND
Created for Use by Professionals
Dairy and Soya Free

MAP № 151 BOSTON TEA PARTY - EDGBASTON

30 Harborne Road, Birmingham, West Midlands, B15 3AA

Call off the search for good coffee in Edgbaston and instead make tracks to Boston Tea Party to revel in interior inspo, delicious fodder and great caffeine.

Each of the rooms within this neighbourhood hub has an artsy and unique vibe: if you're riding solo, settle in the cosy pineapple-inspired room; if you've called up the gang for a brunch debrief, stretch out in the bright blue and white space; and if the sun's out, you've a tough decision to make between the bright and airy conservatory and street-side seating.

INSIDE'S tip GLUTEN DODGER? THE ALL-DAY MENU BOASTS LOADS OF WHEAT-FREE OPTIONS

Wherever you choose to hunker down, ordering a coffee is non-negotiable. Bristol's Extract roasts a delish house espresso and seasonal guest especially for the BTP team. If you're skipping caffeine there's a killer decaf available too.

A 19-strong tea list including unusual picks such as dragon well and lapsang souchong offers further alternatives to the mighty bean.

ESTABLISHED
2017

KEY ROASTER
Extract Coffee
Roasters

BREWING METHOD
Espresso, filter

MACHINE
La Marzocco
Linea PB

GRINDER
Mazzer x 3,
Mythos One

OPENING HOURS
Mon-Fri
7.30am-**6.30**pm
Sat **8**am-**6**pm
Sun **9**am-**5**pm

---

www.bostonteaparty.co.uk   T: 01214 556506

f @btpedgbaston   🐦 @btpcafes   📷 @btpedgbaston

MAP No. 152 BOSTON TEA PARTY - HARBORNE

The School Yard, 106 High Street, Harborne, Birmingham, West Midlands, B17 9NJ

This Harborne hangout (in a Grade II-listed former school building) may be out of walking range of the city centre, but it still beckons intrepid coffee folk in search of quality caffeine.

The intoxicating waft of freshly pulled espresso lures in brew buffs, while the warm and welcoming atmosphere, not-so-secret garden and menu fat with local fodder keeps hungry regulars sweet for a second helping.

INSIDER'S tip KEEP UP TO DATE WITH THE NUMBER OF CUPS SAVED FROM LANDFILL VIA THE WEBSITE

BTP's fairly recent decision to ban disposable cups across its 22 branches was a massive success and has been eagerly embraced by the eco-conscious community of Harborne. Since saving over 200,000 cups (and counting) from going to landfill, the team have turned to tackling plastic waste and swapped milk bottles for 13-litre reusable milk containers.

Pack a KeepCup and reward your good efforts with a beautifully smooth Extract house-blend flat white and a sugar-crusted cinnamon knot from a counter stacked with goodies.

ESTABLISHED
2014

KEY ROASTER
Extract Coffee Roasters

BREWING METHOD
Espresso, filter

MACHINE
La Marzocco Linea PB

GRINDER
Mythos One, Mazzer Luigi

OPENING HOURS
Mon-Sat **8**am-**7**pm
Sun **9**am-**6**pm

www.bostonteaparty.co.uk   T: 01214 278722

f @bostonteaparty 🐦 @btpcafes 📷 @btpharborne

MAP N° 153 THE EARLY BIRD

28 High Street, Kings Heath, Birmingham, West Midlands, B14 7JT

Ever since this artisan bakery launched on Kings Heath High Street in 2018, locals have sacrificed their precious Saturday morning lie-ins to join the queue of patisserie purists awaiting their weekly fix.

Having first pick of the selection of house-made brioche, danish and gateaux isn't the only reason the cafe is crammed come the weekend, as the Early Bird brunch has a loyal following all of its own. Cinnamon-roll french toast, ginger beer-infused bacon rolls and sweetcorn fritters fight it out for the spotlight.

INSIDER'S tip WORD ON THE STREET IS THAT THERE'S A PUDDING CLUB COMING SOON. SIGN. US. UP.

Whether you go sweet or savoury, locally roasted coffee from Hundred House makes an epic pairing. Start the weekend as you mean to go on with a silky flat white and a passionfruit curd and lime sugar cronut, or match a lunchtime salad of curry roasted cauliflower, new potatoes, green beans, pomegranate and crispy shallots with a whistle-clean V60 filter.

Visit mid-week and bagging one of the brown leather banquettes should be easy – your only difficulty will be choosing between the sweet masterpieces behind the glass counter.

ESTABLISHED
2018

KEY ROASTER
Hundred House Coffee

BREWING METHOD
Espresso, V60

MACHINE
La Marzocco Linea Classic

GRINDER
Anfim

OPENING HOURS
Tue-Fri 9am-5pm
Sat 9.30am-5pm
Sun 10am-4pm

Gluten FREE

BEANS AVAILABLE
INSTORE

WIFI

OUTDOOR seating

DISABLED ACCESS

www.theearlybirdbakery.co.uk

f @theearlybirdbakery @theearlybirdbakery

MAP № 154 BREW TWENTY THREE

Cranmore Place, Cranmore Drive, Shirley, West Midlands, B90 4RZ

Speciality grade espresso makes a great bedfellow for the menu of freshly blitzed smoothies, healthy homemade food and delicious bakes at this new Solihull hangout.

Pendant lighting, grey marbled tables and a white tiled bar create a slice of London coffee culture in the heart of the Midlands. Ensuring that the coffee offering also hits city standards is an organic house blend from Grumpy Mule, as well as a seasonal guest espresso.

INSIDER'S TIP GO FOR A BREW BERRY GLOW SMOOTHIE OF MIXED BERRIES, BANANA, DATES AND COCONUT WATER

The health conscious can choose from a colourful line-up of superfood lattes before tucking in to locally baked artisan bread stuffed with free-range chicken, grilled halloumi or veggie options. If something sweeter is called for, a selection of gluten-free and vegan brownies, cakes and raw bites is on hand.

Plant-based? Alt milks come at no extra cost and there are a few options to choose from.

ESTABLISHED
2019

KEY ROASTER
Grumpy Mule

BREWING METHOD
Espresso,
cold brew

MACHINE
La Marzocco
Linea PB

GRINDER
Mahlkonig K30
Twin

OPENING HOURS
Mon-Fri
7.30am-6.30pm
Sat 7.30am-1pm

f @brewtwentythree   @brewtwentythree

MAP№ 155 BOSTON TEA PARTY - SOLIHULL

Herbert Road, Solihull, West Midlands, B91 3QE

Thanks to its fiercely loyal following and reputation for a consistently great cup, it's no surprise that Solihull's BTP tops the local TripAdvisor table when it comes to coffee.

The converted coach house is a charming setting in which to enjoy a carefully crafted flat white or filter brew: natural light tumbles through large windows while original fixtures and fittings add to the rustic and homely vibe. And, in the middle of it all, a counter groaning under the weight of drool-worthy bakes and pastries forms a handsome centrepiece.

INSIDER'S tip THE FAMILY-FRIENDLY VENUE FEATURES A DEDICATED CHILDREN'S PLAY CORNER

The hoppers are kept lively with beans from Bristol's Extract Coffee Roasters. Choose between the house espresso and seasonal guests such as the fruity Unkle Funka.

While the baristas fashion silky flat whites, the kitchen squad whip up delicious grub for an all-day menu which includes plenty of vibrant plant-based plates – the za'atar flatbread studded with toasted sesame seeds, pickled red onion, butternut falafel and hummus is a must.

ESTABLISHED
2018

KEY ROASTER
Extract Coffee Roasters

BREWING METHOD
Espresso, filter

MACHINE
La Marzocco Linea

GRINDER
Victoria Arduino Mythos One, Mazzer Luigi

OPENING HOURS
Mon-Sat 8am-6pm
Sun 9am-5pm

Gluten FREE

BEANS AVAILABLE INSTORE

WIFI

CYCLE FRIENDLY

OUTDOOR Seating

DISABLED ACCESS

BRING YOUR OWN Cup

DOG FRIENDLY

www.bostonteaparty.co.uk   T: 01217 091552
f @btpsolihull 🐦 @btpcafes 📷 @btpsolihull

№156 BEAN & LEAF COFFEE HOUSE

76 Hertford Street, Coventry, West Midlands, CV1 1LB

Feeling the midweek slump? Need a sweet pick-me-up? Take this as your opportunity to wrap yourself in a blanket, get immersed in a great read and savour a standout espresso.

Owners Alisa and Sam Smith have decked out Bean & Leaf with Scandi-style furnishings, houseplants, books and throws to create contemporary hygge cosiness. It's the kind of place where visitors feel totally at ease to step away from the daily grind and take a little time for themselves – with great coffee to hand.

INSIDER'S TIP LOOK OUT FOR ORIGIN CUPPING SESSIONS AND LATTE ART THROWDOWNS

Keep the tempo leisurely and savour a guest filter; the line-up changes weekly and includes UK indies such as Colonna, Round Hill, Bailies, Square Mile and Kiss the Hippo.

Head downstairs to the below-ground seating area and feel seriously snug (and smug) as you indulge in the sticky-fingered thrill of bejewelled traycakes and decadently layered pastries. And should you reach caffeine overload, balance it with the indulgent hit of a Mörk speciality hot chocolate.

ESTABLISHED
2018

KEY ROASTER
Origin Coffee Roasters

BREWING METHOD
Espresso, V60, batch brew, Kalita Wave, AeroPress, Clever Dripper

MACHINE
La Marzocco Linea PB

GRINDER
Mythos One, Mahlkonig EK43

OPENING HOURS
Mon-Fri 8am-6pm
Sat 10am-5pm

---

www.beanandleafcoffeehouse.co.uk T: 07894 881495

f @beanandleafcoffeehouse @ @beanandleafcoffeehouse

MAP № 157 ESPRESSO BARN

Station Road, Long Marston, Stratford-upon-Avon, Warwickshire, CV37 8RP

The wood-clad, bare-walled, concrete-floored charm of this rural find is the epitome of rustic-industrial chic. Bespoke leather-and-coffee-sack-stools and squishy armchairs invite you to take a load off while enjoying an outstanding brew.

Attached to an antiques centre, this middle-of-the-countryside spot attracts day-trippers, dog walkers and cyclists to its sunny courtyard. The team, having cut their teeth at Espresso's collection of train station outposts, certainly know how to deliver consistency, excellence and a friendly vibe.

INSIDER'S tip WATCH THIS SPACE FOR SISTER VENUES AT UMBERSLADE FARM PARK AND THE JEWELLERY QUARTER

Monsoon Estates (from nearby Stratford-upon-Avon) supplies the house blend, Vernal Vibe. Take it as an espresso based drink crafted on the La Spaziale, or plump for AeroPress or Clever Dripper as your serve style of choice.

Homemade cakes – including carrot and walnut, and lemon drizzle – are pleasingly homely and satisfying, but if you've arrived by bike it would be rude not to refuel via the full English breakfast.

ESTABLISHED
2018

KEY ROASTER
Monsoon Estates

BREWING METHOD
Espresso, Clever Dripper, AeroPress

MACHINE
La Spaziale TA S5

GRINDER
Mahlkonig Vario K30

OPENING HOURS
Tue-Sun **10**am-**5**pm

www.caffeideas.com T: 01789 720256

f @espressobarn 🐦 @caffeideas_1 📷 @espressobarnlongmarston

ROASTERS

GIESEN

158 CARRARA COLLECTION

Unit M1 Harrison Road, Airfield Business Park, Market Harborough, Leicestershire, LE16 7QB

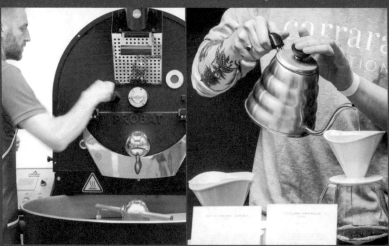

'**C**harmingly British, authentically Italian' is the motto at Carrara. It's a fitting phrase for the family-run Leicestershire roastery which has its roots in the Tuscan town of Lucca.

'From start to finish, our roasting process is all about attention to detail,' says founder Paul. 'We take time and care to bring out the natural characteristics of each coffee.'

Years of tinkering to find the coffee sweet spot have created a balanced house blend called Dimora (rich notes of milk chocolate and caramel with a sweet honey finish) of which Paul and the team are extremely proud.

"WE TAKE TIME TO BRING OUT THE NATURAL CHARACTERISTICS OF EACH COFFEE"

Home brewers can taste the latest single origin lots via the Discover Subscription, or pick what they fancy from the online shop where they can choose specific grind sizes for espresso, drip and cafetiere.

The roastery also welcomes clients for training sessions and cuppings, while coffee-curious members of the public who want to brush up their barista skills can book a masterclass.

ESTABLISHED
2008

ROASTER
MAKE & SIZE
Probat
Probatone 12kg

www.carraracollection.com   01858 469006

@carraracollection   @caffecarrara   @carraracollection

NØRTH Kitchen + Bar № 145

159 QUARTER HORSE COFFEE

88-90 Bristol Street, Birmingham, West Midlands, B5 7AH

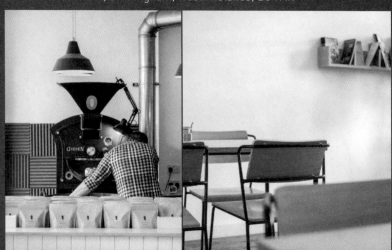

After two years pulling espresso and crafting filters at their Oxford coffee shop, Quarter Horse founders Nathan and Ameeta relocated to Ameeta's hometown of Birmingham to fulfil their dream of roasting the coffee they serve.

Nothing beats sipping an expertly prepared espresso while enjoying the mesmeric whir of the roaster, and their roomy venue (a short stroll from the city centre) was one of the first cafe/roastery hybrids to open outside of London.

Nathan and team fire up the Giesen two to three times a week, carefully bronzing beans for HQ as well as for a string of speciality coffee shops and wholesale partners.

ESTABLISHED
2012

ROASTER
MAKE & SIZE
Giesen W15A
15kg

CAFE ONSITE

OPEN BY APPOINTMENT

COFFEE COURSES

BEANS AVAILABLE

"QUARTER HORSE WAS ONE OF THE FIRST CAFE/ROASTERY HYBRIDS OUTSIDE OF LONDON"

The experience is enhanced by the fact that the huge range of single origins and blends have been selected and roasted by Q grader Nathan (he recently gained his creds), with many of them sourced from women-producer lots. If you can't make it to HQ, order the latest batch online.

www.quarterhorsecoffee.com   01214 489660

@Quarter Horse Coffee   @qtrhorsecoffee   @quarterhorsecoffee

160 HASBEAN

Unit 16, Ladford Covert, Ladfordfields Industrial Estate, Stafford, Staffordshire, ST18 9QL

From humble beginnings experimenting with roasting beans in his garage in the early noughties, Steve Leighton has become a speciality pioneer and the creator of one of Europe's most widely recognised coffee brands.

Steve's Staffordshire roastery boasts an impressive menagerie of chunky machines on which directly sourced beans are carefully cooked.

HASBEAN COFFEES HAVE HELPED TWO BARISTAS SCOOP THE WBC TITLE

Recently gaining organic certification, Hasbean's huge selection of beans offers something for every kind of coffee fan. Whether you're up for a weird and wonderful single origin or prefer a reliable blend for a consistent cup, every bag in the 35-strong line-up is roasted to order.

It's not just home brewers and speciality coffee shop owners who love experimenting with these bronzed beauties either: Hasbean coffees have also helped two baristas scoop the World Barista Championships title – including, in 2017, Dale Harris, Hasbean's own director of wholesale.

ESTABLISHED
2005

ROASTER
MAKE & SIZE
Probat G60 60kg
Probat L25 25kg
Probat P12 12kg
Ambex YM-H2 2kg
Vintage Probat
Vintage Pinhalense

www.hasbean.co.uk   08452 022326

@hasbeancoffee   @hasbean   @hasbean

№ 161 COURTYARD COFFEE ROASTERS

14d High Street, Eccleshall, Staffordshire, ST21 6BZ

Courtyard founder David Wiggins' adventures in coffee began 40 years ago, when he started cooking up green beans on an open-flame Uno roaster in the cellar of his Stoke-on-Trent deli.

In the following decades he tried out many roles within the industry (including opening a cafe and providing coffee for exhibitions) before launching his roastery in 2016.

It's a one-man set-up – though son Daniel lends a hand at events – and David spends his days coaxing flavours out of the beans in his cherry-red Diedrich.

The tiny 300sqft roastery is chocka with bygone roasting paraphernalia – book an appointment for a snoop and to see the magic happen at one of the roasting sessions.

'THE TINY ROASTERY IS CHOCKA WITH BYGONE ROASTING PARAPHERNALIA'

David favours a medium roast yielding rich toasty flavours with sweet notes. Single origins include Indian Balanoor and the Brazilian Ipanema with its dominant note of red grape.

ESTABLISHED
2015

ROASTER MAKE & SIZE
Diedrich 2.5kg

CAFE ONSITE

OPEN SEASONALLY

COFFEE COURSES

BEANS AVAILABLE

www.courtyardcoffeeroasters.co.uk | 01785 851024

@courtyard coffee | @courtyardcoffeeroasters.co.uk

ARTISAN COFFEE

SENSORY & RY

SHROPSHIRE
HEREFORDSHIRE
& WORCESTERSHIRE

Sensory & Rye №167

Worksop

Nottingham

Derby

Burton upon Trent

ull

Locations are approximate

№162 LIAR LIAR

2 Albion Hill, Oswestry, Shropshire, SY11 1QA

Good coffee was thin on the ground in Oswestry before Liar Liar launched in 2016.

Falling down the speciality rabbit hole after helping his stepfather set up a cafe in his antiques emporium, founder Tom Jones made the pilgrimage to Taylor St in London to hone his coffee craft. Returning home – by way of Bristol and a short stint at Boston Tea Party – Tom ended up bagging the keys to a charming corner spot at the heart of the market town.

INSIDER'S TIP RESIDENT FRENCHIE KIKI CAN OFTEN BE FOUND CHILLING IN THE WINDOW

The two-storey space has become a hub for brilliant coffee on the English/Welsh border and Tom and team brew single origin beans from some of the best roasteries around. Regional stars such as Hundred House and Ancoats rub shoulders with guests like Round Hill and Extract.

The team sublet a shared kitchen to other start-ups who craft an exciting bill of eats. The community ethos continues at the bar with a Pay It Forward scheme which donates a coffee to someone in need.

ESTABLISHED
2016

KEY ROASTER
Multiple roasters

BREWING METHOD
Espresso, V60, batch brew, AeroPress

MACHINE
La Marzocco Linea PB

GRINDER
Mythos

OPENING HOURS
Mon-Sat 8.30am-4pm

Gluten FREE

BEANS AVAILABLE INSTORE

 WIFI

 CYCLE FRIENDLY

OUTDOOR seating

COFFEE COURSES

 DOG FRIENDLY

T: 07845 666620
f @liarliaroswestry @liarliaroswestry

MAP № 163 THE SHEWSBURY COFFEEHOUSE

5 Castle Gates, Shrewsbury, Shropshire, SY1 2AE

Cross Shrewsbury Coffeehouse's distinctive green threshold to discover a venue that embodies indie cafe culture and a relaxed approach to life.

Owners Anika and Olivia took over the business in 2018. Their ambition? To bring people together over quality coffee while simultaneously championing the area's small independents. The result is a buzzing hub which has become a little community all of its own.

INSIDER'S TIP CHECK OUT THE ROTATING EXHIBITIONS FROM LOCAL ARTISTS

Style-wise it's a case of industrial grunge meets vintage chic, with lightbulb letters advertising FOOD and COFFEE to passersby. It delivers on the promise with a menu of experimental brunch plates and freshly pulled Hasbean coffee via the La Marzocco machine.

Four-legged regulars are welcome too and might even snap up the highly coveted Dog of the Month award. There's also a line-up of music events and food pop-ups.

ESTABLISHED
2011

KEY ROASTER
Hasbean

BREWING METHOD
Espresso

MACHINE
La Marzocco

GRINDER
Mythos One

OPENING HOURS
Mon-Fri
7.30am-5.30pm
Sat 8am-5.30pm
Sun 10am-4pm

 Gluten FREE
 BEANS AVAILABLE INSTORE
 WIFI
 OUTDOOR seating
 BRING YOUR OWN Cup.
 DOG FRIENDLY

T: 01743 242610
f @theshrewsburycoffeehouse @theshrewsburycoffeehouse

№164 GINGER & CO.

30-31 Princess Street, Shrewsbury, Shropshire, SY1 1LW

Photo: Andy Hughes

Great coffee, delicious homemade grub and good vibes make this Shrewsbury coffee house a triple threat.

So it should come as no surprise to find it spilling over with coffee enthusiasts sipping velvety flat whites, tucking in to bejewelled slabs of carrot cake and chatting to the friendly baristas.

Founders Sam and Kate Gwilliam set out to create a space the whole community could enjoy, and Ginger & Co. (named after Sam's auburn locks) has become a much-loved addition to the area. It's been awarded Best Coffee Shop in Shropshire and is also one of the pioneering businesses to get behind The Shrewsbury Cup reuse scheme.

INSIDER'S *tip* THE BANANA AND CARAMEL CAKE HAS BEEN DESCRIBED AS 'EARTH SHATTERING'

While the bar features an armoury of brewing gear, the team are serious about making speciality inclusive. Don't be afraid to ask which roaster is currently guesting in the second grinder and for the best way to sample the house roast from Method. Whatever you go for, pair it with one of the mind-blowingly good homemade brownies.

ESTABLISHED
2015

KEY ROASTER
Method Coffee Roasters

BREWING METHOD
Espresso, V60, french press, batch brew, pourover

MACHINE
La Marzocco Linea AV

GRINDER
Mahlkonig K30, Mahlkonig EK43

OPENING HOURS
Mon-Sat 8.30am-5pm
Sun 10am-4pm

Gluten FREE

BEANS AVAILABLE IN STORE

WIFI

CYCLE FRIENDLY

BRING YOUR OWN Cup

DOG FRIENDLY

T: 07944 784082

f @gingerandcocoffee 🐦 @ginger_and_co_ 📷 @ginger_and_co_coffee

MAP № 165 CSONS

8 Milk Street, Shrewsbury, Shropshire, SY1 1SZ

C affeine connoisseurs love to moan about the standard of restaurant coffee (usually way below that of the food), so this Shrewsbury eatery is enjoying proving them wrong.

Brothers Adam, Ben, Josh and Reuben Crouch launched CSONS (Crouch Sons, FYI) to combine their interests in great food and local produce. Four years on it's a well-loved hub in the Shropshire town, hosting casual cafe lunches and weekend brunches as well as date night dinners and coffee stop-offs.

INSIDER'S TIP FEELING ADVENTUROUS? TRY THE TURKISH-STYLE COPPER POT COFFEE

As the name implies, seasonality takes star billing on the menu and this extends to the coffee created in collaboration with local roastery Hundred House. The signature blend is expertly matched with Mawley Milk to yield a lip-smackingly delicious range of espresso based drinks.

Loose-leaf teas are also of the speciality persuasion and sourced from Hereford's Trumpers Tea. Pair your pick of the drinks menu with a slice of lemon and almond cake with homemade curd and toast your good fortune to have found food and coffee of equal calibre.

ESTABLISHED
2015

KEY ROASTER
Hundred House Coffee

BREWING METHOD
Espresso

MACHINE
La Marzocco Linea

GRINDER
Mahlkonig K30 twin

OPENING HOURS
Mon-Wed 9am-3.30pm
Thu-Sat 9am-10pm
Sun 10am-3pm
(Closed between 4pm-6pm, Thu-Sat)

Gluten FREE

BEANS AVAILABLE INSTORE

WIFI

OUTDOOR SEATING

DISABLED ACCESS

BRING YOUR OWN Cup.

DOG FRIENDLY

---

www.csons-shrewsbury.co.uk   T: 01743 272709

f @csons shrewsbury   🐦 @csonsshrewsbury   📷 @csons_food

MAP № 166 HEATHER & BATCH COFFEE HOUSE

3 Sandford Avenue, Church Stretton, Shropshire, SY6 6BW

Even if you miss the swing sign above the door, the collection of bikes propped against Heather & Batch's red brick exterior will signal that you've reached your destination.

The small town of Church Stretton is always chocka with visiting mountain bikers and ramblers who, fresh from the Shropshire hills, head here for quality caffeine and wholesome food. Those in the know make a beeline for Heather & Batch.

Espresso is sourced from local roaster Hundred House and the seasonal beans travel all of 15 minutes to reach the cafe's duo of grinders. Fellow Shropshire indie producers join the party in house favourites like the Batch Breakfast of Clun Farm eggs, Andrew Francis bacon, grilled chorizo, homemade baked beans and locally baked bread.

INSIDER'S TIP FORGOT YOUR BIKE LOCK? BORROW ONE FROM THE BAR

Dishes on the all-day menu appeal to all kinds of appetites (from three-cheese grilled sarnies to falafel bowls) and each is crafted with nourishing and unfussy ingredients. If you're undecided about what to commit to, the weekly changing Batch Bowl of salad in summer and stew in winter is always a good shout.

ESTABLISHED
2018

KEY ROASTER
Hundred House Coffee

BREWING METHOD
Espresso

MACHINE
La Spaziale S5

GRINDER
La Spaziale, Mahlkonig

OPENING HOURS
Mon-Sat 9am-4pm

Gluten FREE

BEANS AVAILABLE
INSTORE

WIFI

CYCLE FRIENDLY

BRING YOUR OWN cup.

www.heatherandbatch.co.uk   T: 01694 724644

f @heatherandbatch   @ @heatherandbatch

MAP № 167 SENSORY & RYE

Union Street, Hereford, Herefordshire, HR1 2BS

Don't be fooled by Sensory & Rye's artfully compiled buddha bowls or pancakes showered in petal confetti: this is not a case of style over substance.

The Hereford hangout's small band of Insta-savvy chefs take a seasonal approach to their breakfast, brunch and lunch menus, and make the most of local and regional produce to develop dishes that taste as good as they look on the 'gram.

The same focus on quality shines through at the brew bar where skilled baristas use Worcester-roasted beans to craft glossy espresso and juicy filters. Choose between Method's five single origins for filter or sample the house blend as a flat white with gently steamed Bartonsham Farm milk.

INSIDER'S *tip* WANT TO BRUSH UP YOUR BARISTA SKILLS? BOOK A SLOT ON A COFFEE MASTERCLASS

Afternoons at the aesthetically pleasing space are punctuated with glasses of organic wine and local Hereford cider. There's also a sunny terrace for alfresco eating if you can tear yourself away from papping the industrial-chic interiors.

ESTABLISHED
2016

KEY ROASTER
Method Coffee
Roasters

BREWING METHOD
Espresso, V60,
french press,
cold brew

MACHINE
La Marzocco
Linea PB

GRINDER
Mahlkonig EK43,
Mahlkonig K30
Vario

OPENING HOURS
Mon-Fri 8.30am-4pm
Sat 9am-4pm
Sun 10am-3pm

wwww.sensoryandrye.co.uk   T: 01432 509816
f @sensoryandrye   **🐦** @sensoryandrye   **📷** @sensoryandrye

MAP №168 ABBEY ROAD COFFEE

11 Abbey Road, Great Malvern, Worcestershire, WR14 3ES

Tom Floyd ticked off nearly every job going in the coffee industry – pot washer, Starbucks manager, machine salesperson, barista trainer and more – before finally opening his own cafe in 2015.

Located at the foot of the Malvern Hills, Abbey Road quickly became popular with visiting walkers and flagging tourists, as well as locals looking for a lip-smackingly good cup of coffee.

From the start, Tom has worked with Method Coffee Roasters to ensure a consistently delicious supply of speciality beans; the Worcestershire outfit even roasts a bespoke espresso blend for Abbey Road's Aurelia machine. Guest single origins for the snazzy new Mahlkonig grinder are sourced from indie roasters across the country and prepared as V60 or AeroPress.

INSIDER'S TIP LUNCH INCLUDES PLENTY OF YUMMY CHOICES FOR VEGGIES AND VEGANS

Regular visitors know to grab a table in the below-ground cavern and pair their coffee with one of the too-good-to-turn-down homemade cakes. Coffee lovers with a passion for performance, meanwhile, can tickle the keys of the house piano or schedule a trip around one of the weekly open mic nights or poetry jams.

ESTABLISHED
2015

KEY ROASTER
Method Coffee
Roasters

BREWING METHOD
Espresso, V60,
AeroPress

MACHINE
Nuova Simonelli
Aurelia

GRINDER
Mahlkonig
K30 Air,
Nuova Simonelli
Mythos

OPENING HOURS
Mon-Sat **8**am-**5**pm
Sun **9**am-**4**pm

 Gluten FREE

 BEANS AVAILABLE INSTORE

 WIFI

 CYCLE FRIENDLY

 OUTDOOR SEATING

 DOG FRIENDLY

www.abbeyroadcoffee.co.uk   T: 07947 209886
f @abbeyroadcoffee   🐦 @abbeyrdcoffee   📷 @abbeyroadcoffee

MAP 169 METHOD COFFEE ROASTERS

Arch 51, Cherry Tree Walk, Worcester, Worcestershire, WR1 3BH

Coffee fans with an adventurous palate should schedule a trip to this Worcestershire roastery cafe.

A constantly shifting selection of micro-lot single origins and seasonal blends means there's always something new and noteworthy to sample via a roster of serve styles at Method's railway arch HQ. And with the same team roasting and brewing the beans, you can be confident your coffee will be served just as it's meant to be drunk – whether as a clean filter or in an espresso tonic.

INSIDER'S TIP LOOK OUT FOR MONTHLY CUPPING EVENTS FEATURING GUEST SPEAKERS

The gang mostly source their greens from Africa and Central America and enjoy particularly strong links with farms in Guatemala and Colombia. Watch the latest batch of beans being cooked up on the vintage roaster while you sip and snack in the glass-fronted cafe space.

A small list of eats centres around toasties and cakes and takes the same traceable and quality approach as the coffee: bread, cheese, meat and veggies are all sourced from local Herefordshire and Worcestershire producers.

ESTABLISHED
2018

KEY ROASTER
Method Coffee Roasters

BREWING METHOD
Espresso, AeroPress, Chemex, V60

MACHINE
La Marzocco Linea PB ABR

GRINDER
Mahlkonig K30 Air, Mahlkonig Peak, Mahlkonig EK43, Anfim Pratica

OPENING HOURS
Mon-Fri 8am-4pm
Sat 9am-4pm
Sun 10am-4pm

Gluten FREE

BEANS AVAILABLE INSTORE

WIFI

CYCLE FRIENDLY

OUTDOOR seating

DISABLED ACCESS

BRING YOUR OWN CUP

COFFEE COURSES

DOG FRIENDLY

---

www.methodroastery.com T: 01905 780070

f @methodroastery 🐦 @methodroastery 📷 @methodroastery

MAP № 170 WAYLAND'S YARD – WORCESTER

6 Foregate Street, Worcester, Worcestershire, WR1 1DB

There aren't many places where you can sip espresso while swaying on a swing or tuck in to a stack of buttermilk pancakes with your four-legged friend in tow, but there aren't many places like Wayland's Yard.

'Proper coffee. Proper food. Proper people' is the motto here, and creating a space where people can congregate to enjoy expertly prepared coffee and epic brunches with chums has been the aim of owner (and ex pro-rugby player) Sam Smith since he launched Wayland's in 2016.

INSIDER'S tip TRY THE HOT VS COLD FLIGHT: THE SAME BEANS PREPARED AS POUROVER AND COLD BREW

With its spacious courtyard, the coffee shop has become *the* hottest hangout for Worcester's canine contingent. When the sun's out, you'll find their human companions sipping cold brew and feasting on house favourites such as eggy crumpets with smoked chilli jam and griddled halloumi.

Shop dog Kobe ensures everyone has a good time, with a little help from the rabble of friendly baristas. Ask for their pick of the guest roasters (recent residencies include Dark Arts, Neighbourhood and Caravan) or for help planning your event or party in the yard.

ESTABLISHED
2016

KEY ROASTER
Method Coffee Roasters

BREWING METHOD
Espresso, V60, cold brew

MACHINE
La Marzocco Linea PB ABR

GRINDER
Mahlkonig K30,
Mahlkonig EK43,
Mahlkonig Peak

OPENING HOURS
Mon-Fri **7**am-**6**pm
Sat **8**am-**6**pm
Sat **9**am-**5**pm

---

www.waylandsyard.com

f @waylandsyard 🐦 @waylandsyard 📷 @waylandsyard

MAP №171 BAYLEY'S OF BROMSGROVE

6 Worcester Road, Bromsgrove, Worcestershire, B61 7AE

In just a couple of years, the Bayley brothers have shaken up Bromsgrove's indie scene. Indulging their passions for great caffeine and craft beer – with the help of an awesome team – they've created a lively hub where locals can catch up over Birmingham-roasted coffee and regionally brewed beer.

Inside the coffee shop/tap room hybrid there's a kick-back-and-relax vibe thanks to the rabble of friendly staff, open-plan set-up and waft of freshly ground coffee from the Mythos grinder. Quarter Horse keeps the hopper humming with its Dark Horse Espresso, while guest appearances come from the likes of Caravan and Dark Arts.

INSIDER'S TIP PICKING UP BEANS FOR THE ROAD? ASK NICELY AND THE BARISTAS WILL GRIND THEM TO ORDER

If you're looking for a drink with an ABV, a help-yourself fridge stocks a huge selection of craft beers and ales to drink in or take out. There's also a cage of spirits and a killer drinks list to get the party started.

The day-to-evening concept is going down so well that the crew are expanding into the unit next door. Plans for Bayley's 2.0 include an extra bar area, local food vendor pop-ups and movie nights.

ESTABLISHED
2017

KEY ROASTER
Quarter Horse
Coffee

BREWING METHOD
Espresso, V60,
AeroPress

MACHINE
La Marzocco
Linea PB

GRINDER
Nuova Simonelli
Mythos One

OPENING HOURS
Tue-Thu 10am-10pm
Fri-Sat 10am-11pm

Gluten FREE

BEANS AVAILABLE INSTORE

WIFI

CYCLE FRIENDLY

OUTDOOR seating

DISABLED ACCESS

DOG FRIENDLY

f @bayleysbromsgrove 🐦 @bayleysofbrom 📷 @bayleys_of_bromsgrove

ROASTERS

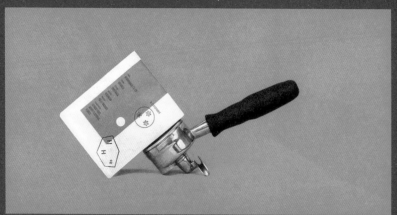

In addition to roasting single estate micro-lots, fusing adventurous espresso blends and building relationships with farmers at origin, this multi-award winning roastery has also developed a stream of not-for-profit creative projects.

Through its pioneering programme, Hundred House offers educational and creative initiatives which shed light on sustainable coffee trading practices and raise awareness through visual arts and design.

'We work with art and design entities to create spaces that invite social and cultural dialogue – coupled with great coffee,' says director Matthew Wade.

'SOCIAL AND CULTURAL DIALOGUE – COUPLED WITH GREAT COFFEE'

The roastery supports the arts through industry, with a series of commissions, inner-city school programmes, planned residencies and events aimed at making connections between the creative and the industrial.

'Our education programme is driven towards conversations that contribute to a healthier synthesis of communities across the globe, and which educate the next generation about the importance of trading fairly and being conscious of where our food and drink comes from,' adds Matthew.

ESTABLISHED
2016

ROASTER
MAKE & SIZE
Diedrich IR-12
12kg

---

www.hundredhousecoffee.com   01584 841206

@hundredhousecoffee   @hundredhouseco   @hundredhousecoffee

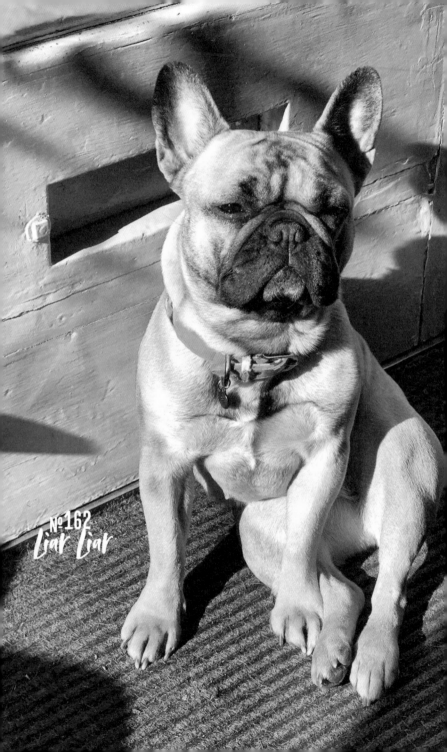

№162
Liar Liar

173 METHOD COFFEE ROASTERS

Arches 50-51, Cherry Tree Walk, Worcester, Worcestershire, WR1 3BH

Such is the demand for Method's small batch beans that, in order to keep up, the Worcestershire roastery has already moved twice – and it only launched in 2014.

Its new HQ is in a couple of repurposed Victorian railway arches. The increased space has allowed the team to open a dedicated cupping lab and training facilities, as well as to make room for the chunky 25kg refurbished vintage Probat.

'A PARTNERSHIP IN GUATEMALA HAS YIELDED A CROP OF SERIOUSLY SPECIAL MICRO-LOTS'

'Quality with provenance' is the Method mantra and ensuring all of the coffees destined for the roaster are sustainably and ethically sourced is priority number one. A partnership in Guatemala is the latest project to yield a crop of seriously special micro-lots.

While the gang love to play with rare finds, the seasonal Hay Espresso levels out Method's offering with crowd-pleasing caramel sweetness and chocolatey body. Home brewers can take one of the regular coffee classes and learn from the pros how to make the most of their Method beans.

ESTABLISHED
2014

ROASTER
MAKE & SIZE
Vintage Probat
UG22 25kg

CAFÉ ONSITE

OPEN BY APPOINTMENT

COFFEE COURSES

BEANS AVAILABLE
ONLINE / IN-STORE

www.methodroastery.com | 01905 780070

@methodroastery   @methodroastery   @methodroastery

MORE GOOD

COFFEEHOUSE & ROASTERIES

№114
Out of the Woods
— Granary Wharf

MORE GOOD
COFFEE SHOPS
MORE EXCEPTIONAL PLACES TO DRINK COFFEE ...

174
1901 CAFFE BISTRO
68 St. George's Terrace, Jesmond,
Newcastle upon Tyne, NE2 2DL
www.1901caffe.co.uk

175
92 DEGREES – HARDMAN STREET
24 Hardman Street, Liverpool, L1 9AX
www.92degreescoffee.com

176
92 DEGREES – JAMAICA STREET
49 Jamaica Street, Liverpool, L1 0AH
www.92degreescoffee.com

177
ATKINSONS – THE CASTLE
Lancaster Castle, Castle Hill,
Lancaster, LA1 1YN
www.thecoffeehopper.com

178
BACKYARD BIKE SHOP
Hillgate Quay, Gateshead, NE8 2BH
www.backyardbikeshop.com

179
BALTZERSEN'S
22 Oxford Street, Harrogate, HG1 1PU
www.baltzersens.co.uk

180
BASECAMP COFFI
36 High Street, Llanberis, LL55 4EU
www.basecampcoffi.co.uk

181
BLOOM
32 Poplar Road, Birmingham, B14 7AD
www.bloomkingsheath.com

182
BOM BOM PATISSERIE
12 Derwent Drive, Loughborough, LE11 3RJ
www.bombompatisserie.com

183
BOO BOO COFFEE
27 Lordswood Road, Birmingham, B17 9RP
www.boobooharborne.com

184
BOSTON TEA PARTY – WORCESTER
18 Broad Street, Worcester, WR1 3NF
www.bostonteaparty.co.uk

185
BOSTON TEA PARTY – STRATFORD
St Gregory's Hall, Henley Street,
Stratford-upon-Avon, CV37 6QW
www.bostonteaparty.co.uk

186
BURR COFFEE
5 Lendal, York, YO1 8AQ
www.burrcoffee.co.uk

187
CIELO COFFEE HOUSE – GARFORTH
41 Main Street, Garforth, Leeds, LS25 1DS
www.cielouk.com

188
CIELO COFFEE HOUSE – YORK PLACE
18 York Place, Leeds, LS1 2EX
www.cielouk.com

189
EPISODE ONE
83 Great George Street, Leeds, LS1 3BR
www.episodecoffee.co.uk

190
ESPRESSO CORNER
11 Kirkgate, Huddersfield, HD1 1QS

191
EXCHANGE COFFEE COMPANY – BLACKBURN MARKET
Stall F9/1 Blackburn Market,
Ainsworth Street, Blackburn, BB1 5AF
www.exchangecoffee.co.uk

192
EXCHANGE COFFEE COMPANY – TODMORDEN
Todmorden Market Hall, Burnley Road,
Todmorden, OL14 5AJ
www.exchangecoffee.co.uk

193
EZRA & GIL
20 Hilton Street, Northern Quarter,
Manchester, M1 1FR
www.ezraandgil.com

194
FLAT WHITE KITCHEN
40 Saddler Street, Durham, DH1 3NU
www.flatwhitekitchen.com

195
GRASSHOPPER CAFE
18 Castleton Road, Hope, Hope Valley, S33 6RD

196
HOXTON NORTH
1a Royal Parade, Harrogate, HG1 2SZ
www.hoxtonnorth.com

197
JOE'SPRESSO
404b South Road, Walkley, Sheffield, S6 3TF
www.joespresso.co.uk

198
LA BOTTEGA MILANESE – THE LIGHT
The Headrow, Leeds, LS1 8TL
www.labottegamilanese.co.uk

199
LANEWAY & CO
17-19 High Bridge,
Newcastle upon Tyne, NE1 1EW

200
LONGFORD
Longford Place, Rusholme,
Manchester, M14 5GG

201
MANCOCO
84 Hewitt Street, Manchester, M15 4GB
www.mancoco.co.uk

202
MARMADUKES CAFE DELI
22 Norfolk Row, Sheffield, S1 2PA
www.marmadukes.co

203
MRS ATHA'S
18 Central Road, Leeds, LS1 6DE
www.mrsathasleeds.com

204
NORTH STAR COFFEE
Unit 33, Leeds Dock, The Boulevard, Leeds, LS10 1PZ
www.northstarroast.com

205
ONE PERCENT FOREST
42 Allerton Road, Woolton, Liverpool, L25 7RG
www.onepercentforest.co.uk

206
PILGRIM'S COFFEE HOUSE
Marygate, The Holy Island of Lindisfarne, TD15 2SJ
www.pilgrimscoffee.com

207
SALAMI & CO.
10 Market Place, Otley, LS21 3AQ
www.salamiandco.com

208
SIFT CAFE & BAKERY
11 Manor Square, Otley, LS21 3AP
www.siftotley.com

209
SIX EIGHT KAFE
Floor 2, Milennium Point, Curzon Street,
Birmingham, B4 7XG
www.sixeightkafe.co.uk

210
STAGE COFFEE
41 Great George Street, Leeds, LS1 3BB
www.stagecoffee.com

211
STEAM ROOM COFFEE
181 Knightlow Road, Birmingham, B17 8PY
www.steamroomcoffee.co.uk

212
STEAM YARD
Unit 1-2 Aberdeen Court,
97 Division Street, Sheffield, S1 4GE
www.steamyard.co.uk

213
THE ANCHOR COFFEE HOUSE
508 Moss Lane East, Manchester, M14 4PA
www.anchorcoffee.co.uk

214
THE FLOWER CUP
61 Watergate Row South, Chester, CH1 2LE
www.flowercup.co.uk

215
THE FOSSGATE SOCIAL
25 Fossgate, York, YO1 9TA
www.thefossgatesocial.com

216
THE SPECIALITY COFFEE SHOP
50 Friar Lane, Nottingham, NG1 6DQ
www.thespecialtycoffeeshop.com

217
TOP DOOR ESPRESSO
Indoor Shop 45, Halifax Borough Market,
Halifax, HX1 1DZ
www.topdoorespresso.uk

218
TOWN HOUSE COFFEE & BREW BAR
62 Friargate, Preston, PR1 2AT

219
TROVE
5 Murray Street, Ancoats, Manchester, M4 6HS
www.trovefoods.co.uk

220
TWO CHIMPS COFFEE
8b Oakham Enterprise Park, Ashwell
Road, Oakham, LE15 7TU
www.twochimpscoffee.com

221
URBAN EMPORIUMS
30 Church Street, Birmingham, B3 2NP
www.urbanemporiums.com

222
WARWICK STREET KITCHEN
102 Warwick Street, Leamington Spa, CV32 4QP
www.warwickstreetkitchen.com

MORE GOOD
ROASTERIES

ADDITIONAL BEANS FOR YOUR HOME HOPPER

ANCOATS COFFEE CO.

9 Royal Mills, 17 Redhill Street,
Manchester, M4 5BA

www.ancoats-coffee.co.uk

BEAN BROTHERS COFFEE COMPANY

Fairfield Mills, Colne Road,
Huddersfield, HD1 3DX

www.beanbrothers.co.uk

BUXTON ROASTERY

Unit 20b Kiln Lane, Harpur Hill Business
Park, Buxton, SK17 9JL

www.buxtonroastery.co.uk

CARTWHEEL

Unit S1, Roden House, Roden Street, Sneinton,
Nottingham, NG3 1JH

www.cartwheelcoffee.com

CIELO COFFEE ROASTERS

41 Main Street, Garforth, Leeds, LS25 1DS

www.cielouk.com

COFFI ERYRI

Nebo, Llanrwst, Conwy, North Wales

www.coffieryri.cymru

HEART AND GRAFT COFFEE ROASTERY

30 Holyoak Street, Manchester, M40 1HB

www.heartandgraft.co.uk

JOLLY BEAN ROASTERY

15 Victoria Road, Saltaire, BD18 3LQ

www.jollybeanroastery.co.uk

MANCOCO

Arch 84, Hewitt Street, Manchester, M15 4GB

www.mancoco.co.uk

MAUDE COFFEE ROASTERS

82-83 Railway Street, Leeds, LS9 8HB

www.maudecoffee.co.uk

MONSOON ESTATES COFFEE COMPANY

The Studio Alscot Park, Atherstone on Stour,
Stratford-upon-Avon, CV37 8BL

www.monsoonestatescoffee.co.uk

NORTH STAR COFFEE ROASTERS

Unit 10, 280 Tong Road, Leeds, LS12 3BG

www.northstarroast.com

NORTHERN EDGE COFFEE

Unit 3, Samphire Court, Windmill Way,
Ramparts Business Park,
Berwick-upon-Tweed, TD15 1TB

www.northernedgecoffee.co.uk

OUSEBURN COFFEE CO.

Unit 25, Albion Row,
Newcastle upon Tyne, NE6 1LQ

www.ouseburncoffee.co.uk

POCOESPRESSO

29 The Gables, Cottam, Preston, PR4 0LG

www.pocoespresso.com

RED KITE COFFEE ROASTERS

The Coach House, Regent Terrace,
Harrogate, HG1 4BL

www.redkiteroasters.co.uk

ROUNTON COFFEE ROASTERS

East Rounton, Northallerton, DL6 2LG

www.rountoncoffee.co.uk

SMITH STREET COFFEE ROASTERS

30 Scotland Street, Sheffield, S3 7AA

www.smithstreetcoffeeroasters.co.uk

STEWARTS OF TRENT BRIDGE COFFEE ROASTERS

Unit 31, Avenue C, Sneinton Market,
Nottingham, NG1 1DW

www.stewartscoffees.co.uk

Roost Coffee N°. 120 & Roastery

MEET
OUR
COMMITTEE

Our *Independent Coffee Guide* committee is made up of a small band of leading coffee experts from across the region who have worked with Salt Media and the coffee community to oversee the creation of this year's guide

Having worked in the speciality sector since 2013, Sonali has progressed from wholesale account management to coffee education and training. Passionate about creating more awareness around mental health, she's initiated conversations via regular panel discussions with members of the hospitality industry across the UK.

Sonali is as interested in food as coffee and hosts regular supper clubs.

Fine art graduate Matthew trained as a barista and roaster in New Zealand. He brought his experience back to London and played a leading role in the burgeoning coffee scene in the early noughties.

Matthew became one of the UK's first Q graders and won several awards for his coffees when he was head roaster at Union Hand-Roasted and Bullet Coffee. In 2011 he moved to the Middle East and was instrumental in developing its nascent third wave coffee movement, as well as co-founding Dubai's Nightjar Coffee. On his return to the UK in 2016, Matthew set up Hundred House Coffee, a multi-award winning roastery in Shropshire.

Dave Olejnik

Hannah Davies

Having always sought out great coffee shops, it was during Dave's time living in Seattle (where he worked as a touring guitar tech) that he was inspired to divert his energies into coffee full time. Returning to the UK, he worked for Coffee Community and travelled the world as a trainer and consultant before launching Laynes Espresso in Leeds in 2011. Dave opened his second venue, Dot the Lions, within Leeds Arts University in 2019 and is gearing up to open Sarto (a coffee, craft beer, wine and pasta bar).

Hannah's 12-year career in the coffee industry saw her develop from a barista in Liverpool to training manager and authorised SCA trainer for a national coffee company. Her current role as SCA events manager allows her to fulfil her commitment to the coffee community in the UK and across Europe.

Since 2014, Hannah has worked with the Manchester coffee scene to create Manchester Coffee Festival, dedicated to showcasing the speciality coffee industry of the North.

Paul
Meikle-Janney

Ian
Steel

Ian has enjoyed two careers: one as a TV producer and another as a coffee roaster. *'They're both related,'* he says, *'as they involve seeing ideas through from conception to completion.'*

Paul is one of the founders of Dark Woods Coffee, a multi-award winning rural roastery on the outskirts of Huddersfield.

In 1999 Paul started Coffee Community, an international training and consultancy agency for the speciality industry. He's co-written both the City & Guilds and SCA barista qualifications and has been involved in the World and UK Barista Championships since their inception. He was also head judge at the World Latte Art and World Coffee in Good Spirits championships for four years.

When he's not fulfilling SCA Education Committee duties, Paul tends his ever-growing jazz and house record collection.

Standing in the middle of the coffee chain between producer and consumer, Ian sees his responsibility as helping make connections between the two. His goal is for all Atkinsons beans to be 'relationship coffees' and he works with farmers to establish financial and environmental sustainability and full traceability.

Ian is also an entrepreneur-in-residence and honorary teaching fellow at Lancaster University's Management School and a founding member of the Global Eco-Innovation forum.

Coffee
notes

SOMEWHERE TO SAVE DETAILS OF SPECIFIC BREWS
AND BEANS YOU'VE ENJOYED

INDEX